Mary A. R. Rhenher
U of Nevada -
1961.

THE STORY OF ST. THOMAS'S

1106 - 1947

THE STORY OF
ST. THOMAS'S
1106 - 1947

BY

CHARLES GRAVES

*With 8 Plates in Colour
and 41 Illustrations in
Black and White*

DISTRIBUTED BY
FABER AND FABER LTD
FOR ST. THOMAS'S HOSPITAL

DESIGNED AND PRODUCED FOR
ST. THOMAS'S HOSPITAL BY
ADPRINT LIMITED LONDON

DISTRIBUTED BY
FABER AND FABER LIMITED
24 RUSSELL SQUARE, LONDON, W.C.1

ILLUSTRATIONS IN COLOUR

WITH 41 ILLUSTRATIONS IN PHOTOGRAVURE

LIST OF CONTENTS

In St. Mary's Priory, Southwark, whose gateway is shown as it survived in 1811, an infirmary was established before the Norman Conquest. It was to become St. Thomas's Spital

I

"LET GOD BE LOVED, THEN YOUR NEIGHBOUR"

Sт. thomas's hospital survived the Black Death, the Wars of the Roses, the Dissolution of the Monasteries, the Plague and the Great Fire of London. It stoutly refused the nominees of monarch after monarch. For nearly one thousand years this hospital has given refuge and succour to the sick and needy of London.

Of mere brick and stone buildings, there are many examples more ancient, but there is no living entity which can compete with it for sheer age-long service to humanity. No monastery, no convent, no university, no school, no college, not even the Papal Guard can boast a similar pedigree straight back to the reign of King Stephen, nor shew the same proud devotion to duty in spite of every handicap caused down the centuries by poverty, epidemics, wars and fundamental changes in the Constitution.

Now, after centuries of unremitting voluntary service to the citizens of London, St. Thomas's is on the threshold of a new career under State control. Verily, the old order changeth . . .

Hospitals have always provided the most practical form of Christianity ever preached by the Church and, indeed, owe their origin to the religious Houses of former days. St. Thomas's is no exception, though the original conception of the ancient monastic Orders was, of course, somewhat selfish. Virtuous men—and women—withdrew entirely from the outside world to

9

save their own souls. Whereupon, deprived of lay doctors, it was only natural that they should acquire some primitive knowledge of medicine and practise it to protect themselves from illness.

The next step was very human. Being intrinsically good people, the monks and nuns could scarcely refuse succour to needy wayfarers. (A modern example of this physical form of assistance is provided by the St. Bernard dogs of the Hospice of St. Bernard in Switzerland.) Not surprisingly, therefore, the clinical knowledge which the members of these religious Orders acquired for their own self-protection was used not merely for the benefit of the unfortunates who were passing through the region, but also for the hurt and maimed who lived in the neighbourhood and who, seeing what was done for strangers, pleaded for similar treatment.

Thus it was that nearly one thousand years ago the Priory of St. Mary the Virgin found that so much of its time was being devoted to looking after the sick and needy travellers who entered the City of London over the only bridge from the South—the ancient Roman bridge of Southwark—that it was necessary first to enlarge the infirmary, and then to erect a separate building devoted entirely to the ill and lame entering London from that quarter. This part of the Priory, situated on the site now occupied by Southwark Cathedral, and known as St. Thomas's Spital from the time of Thomas à Becket's canonization in 1173, had existed for charitable work and primitive healing since before the Norman Conquest, when Winchester was the capital of southern England and London was just a large trading post continually besieged by the Danes.

But as time passed London grew, and more and larger demands were made on the time of the brethren. Fortunately, the Order of Augustine Canons, which had founded the Priory of St. Mary the Virgin, was specially adapted to minister to the sick because its rule was much less self-centred and lighter in spiritual duties than that of the monks, as is shewn by the opening clause of St. Augustine, their founder, which reads: "Before all things, dearest Brethren, let God be loved, *then your neighbour*." As a result, the brethren were at least a century ahead of the Grey or ministering friars of St. Francis of Assisi. Their infirmary quickly became a hospital for sick persons who were making their way to London and it is noteworthy that when Rahere the Jester founded St. Bartholomew's to play the same part in the north of London in 1123, he staffed it with Augustinian canons.

In those days priests were not allowed to shed blood (the fighting bishops, when they went to war, always used a mace instead of a sword) and it was necessary, in consequence, for all surgery to be handed over to a subordinate not in holy orders. Which is the reason why, even today, the physician takes precedence of the surgeon.

Medicine, for some years after the Conquest, consisted very largely of potions and charms which were thought to be most effective when administered by a priest upon consecrated ground. Some of the drugs were laxative, some sedative, and some tonic or stimulating; they were nearly all vegetable

Dissection in 1495. Though the early hospitals were religious foundations, the duties of the surgeon were always performed by laymen

and often as many as fifteen were found in one prescription. These, no doubt, did good in certain cases though the chief effect of the leechdoms, with their charms and spells, was mental rather than physical.

But it must not be thought that the priestly physician prepared the complicated and often revolting messes which he prescribed. He was far too exalted a person to do anything with his hands and relied upon inspection of his patient from a safe distance and upon an examination of the urine for his diagnosis. Apothecaries, however, began to specialize quite early, and we are told that in 1180 Henry II took one with him to Ireland. Hence we may be sure that one of the lay brothers of the hospital learnt the art of the apothecary and must have had his dispensary, where the various native and foreign drugs were stored. A very favourite prescription was "Hiera Picra", or holy bitters, which, in a simple form, contained aloes, mastic saffron, Indian navel, carpo balsam, and assarum; though for more important cases fourteen ingredients were used. It is probable, therefore, that the hospital apothecary of the twelfth century was quite a busy man.

Black Death or bubonic plague seems to have visited London on several occasions before the great outbreak in 1348, though it was often confused with the famine pestilences in which typhus, dysentery, and enteric carried off a great many victims. In particular, there were severe famines, followed

11

by pestilences, in 1198 and 1258. Sweating sickness too, brought quick death. Then there was leprosy, from which many other conditions were not diagnosed. It seems that the real number of lepers in England at any one time has been greatly exaggerated, partly because so many of them were not lepers at all, and partly because the protracted nature of the disease made one of them go a long way. Special lazar houses were built for them, but these seem always to have sheltered other cases as well. There was a lazar or lock hospital in Kent Street, near Regent's Canal, probably from early in the twelfth century, and to this (no doubt) all leprous cases applying at St. Mary's and St. Thomas's were sent. Whence the "lock hospitals" took their name is an open question. One explanation is that the lazar house in Kent Street stood where a stream or dyke was crossed by the road and that here a sluice or lock was placed.

Syphilis was unrecognized, though sporadic cases may have come into London by sea; since, however, secondary and tertiary cases would almost certainly have been diagnosed as leprosy the sufferers would have been very effectually segregated.

Smallpox was known but was not thought to be infectious until Gilbertus Anglicus, who practised in London until 1250, showed that it was. Probably it was known as "the pox", a name derived from the Old English "póc" or pocket, until syphilis was recognized and spoken of as the "great pox".

When the famous medical school at Salerno was at its height in 1072 that town was captured by the Normans; and soon after this, priests from England were sent there to learn up-to-date medicine, though they must have been few and far between, and it was many years before their knowledge reached Southwark.

The Lock Hospital, Kent Street, in which leprous and other cases were segregated

12

II

THE SUPPORT OF THE GODFEARING

In 1207 a disastrous fire destroyed most of the Priory, and Peter de Rupibus, a professional soldier of fortune who became Bishop of Winchester, realizing that something must be done for the mass of suffering humanity which the hospital had relieved, made an appeal for funds—the first of many during the next seven centuries. This appeal was most successful, for the Bishop remitted twenty days of penance to everybody who contributed to the Fund. With the monies thus raised the Hospital was rebuilt on a site one hundred yards further from the river, where the air was purer and the water more plentiful.

In those days, of course, the hospital was a foundation of the Holy Roman Church and its possessions being, therefore, Church property were much more secure than if they had belonged to a layman. So, as time went on, St. Thomas's acquired an astonishing number of lands and houses bequeathed to it by the godfearing. The hospital itself consisted of a picturesque irregular two-storeyed building of rough-hewn oak and a thatched roof. The forty patients lay in the upper rooms on beds of rushes, the only illumination being from candles made out of the surplus fat from the meat rations. The hospital staff consisted of four canons, three professed sisters and a warden, as well as a lay surgeon, a porter, brewer, baker, cook and lay sisters—the fore-runners of our modern nurses. But, as there were at least three religious services a day and a good many confessions, extreme unctions and funerals to be taken, as well as a certain amount of official begging to be done, the medical staff could not devote much time to leechcraft, which was, perhaps, just as well for the patients.

Beds did not become common until the end of the thirteenth century, when they were occupied by two or even three patients who, in those days, wore no night clothes at all.

The indulgence promised by Peter de Rupibus seems to have been effective for at least one hundred years, for the fourteenth century opened with a continued flow of gifts to the hospital. But that frightful epidemic the Black Death in 1348 must have put terrific pressure on the hospital. It reached London in the November and lasted until the following Whitsun. It was this same bubonic plague which returned in 1665. In many cases, pneumonia set in and it is estimated that twenty thousand people, half the population, died in London alone. Besides killing off a high percentage of the brethren of the hospital, the Black Death caused a great dearth of labourers. This made things even more difficult for those whose income was derived from land, like St. Thomas's. The Prior, therefore, asked Pope Innocent the Sixth to grant no less than two years and eighty days' indulgence to all who would help pay the hospital's debts. The Pope, however, only saw his way to grant an indulgence for one year and forty days. This, incidentally, shows how far the influence of the Pope had waned since Peter de Rupibus had secured substantial subscriptions for only twenty days' indulgence.

There are no records of the treatment of hospital patients in those days, but Chaucer's description of the Doctor of Physic in his *Canterbury Tales* gives a fair idea of how medicine was practised. It will be remembered that the worthy doctor relied on his knowledge of astronomy and astrology as well as on his powers in natural magic. Having first cast the patient's horoscope, he would consider the malady: "Were it of cold, or hot, or moist, or dry, and where engendered and of what humour." After which he would prescribe

St. Thomas's, at this time suppressed by Henry VIII and lying idle, is to the righ

14

"drugges and lectuaries" which were dispensed by his apothecaries. Whether the four Augustinian canons in St. Thomas's ever really studied astrology is doubtful. But no doubt they would have their patients bled on certain days and not on others, for astrological formulæ had largely replaced the incantations and prayers with which drugs were formerly administered.

Their greatest asset, however, was the mass of clinical experience which they could not help acquiring. Plague was always with them and flared up every ten or twelve years, while typhus, enteric, dysentery, scurvy, tubercle, rickets, and malaria kept all their beds occupied. In addition, the Out-Patients' department must have been continuously busy with emergency casualty cases which turbulent and insanitary Southwark provided daily.

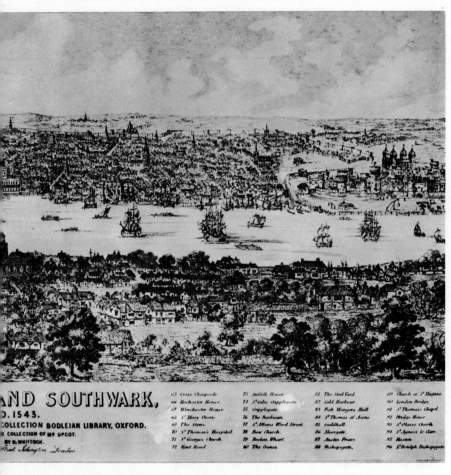

ND SOUTHWARK,
0.1543.
COLLECTION BODLEIAN LIBRARY, OXFORD.
E COLLECTION OF M? UPCOT.
BY B. WHITTOCK.
Prat Islington London

65 *Cross Cheapside*	73 *Suffolk House*	81 *The Steel Yard*	89 *Church of S' Magnus*
66 *Rochester House*	74 *S'Giles Cripplegate*	82 *Cold Harbour*	90 *London Bridge*
67 *Winchester House*	75 *Cripplegate*	83 *Fish Mongers Hall*	91 *S' Thomas's Chapel*
68 *S' Mary Overie*	76 *The Barbican*	84 *S' Thomas of Acons*	92 *Bridge House*
69 *The Stews*	77 *S'.Albans Wood Street*	85 *Guildhall*	93 *S'Olaves Church*
70 *S' Thomas's Hospital*	78 *Bow Church*	86 *Moorgate*	94 *S'Agnes le Clare*
71 *S'Georges Church*	79 *Broken Wharf*	87 *Austin Friars*	95 *Hoxton*
72 *Kent Road*	80 *The Cranes*	88 *Bishopsgate*	96 *S'Botolph Bishopsgate*

f the bridge approach. On the extreme left, towards the river, are the stews

· 15

III

THE KING'S FOUNDATION

In the introduction to "Collections of a London Citizen" published by the Camden Society, page ix, the following passage occurs:

> Thomas Spetylle. And at that same place ys an ospytalyte for pore men and wymmen, and that nobyl marchaunt, Rycharde Whytyngdon, made a newe chambyr with viii beddys for young wemen that had done a-mysse in truste of a good mendement. And he commaundyd thatt alle the thyngys that ben don in that chambyr shulde be kepte secrete with owte forthe, yn payne of lesyng of hyr levynge; for he wolde not shame no yonge women in noo wyse, for hit myght be cause of hyr lettyng [hindrance] of hyr maryage.

Richard Whittington lived between 1358 and 1423, and was four times Mayor of London. The immorality of London, with its stews (houses of ill-fame, dotted all round the neighbourhood of St. Thomas's) was quite unbelievable by modern standards. And as time went on, things grew worse and worse, both inside and outside the hospital. By 1507 St. Thomas's was in a very dilapidated state and new buildings had to be erected on the site of the skittle alley or "closhbanc" of the Faucon Tavern.

It was here that the printing of the first full translation of the Bible into English was completed by Miles Coverdale on the printing press in the precincts of the hospital. But in spite of this worthy work, it is clear that the discipline among the brethren and the sisters in the hospital was by no means good, and on January 14th, 1540, the blow fell. St. Thomas's Hospital and all its possessions in the counties of Surrey, Sussex, Kent, Middlesex, Essex, Cambridge, the City of London, and elsewhere were surrendered to the King during the Dissolution of the Monasteries.

The immediate result was that for eleven years the hospital lay derelict. Its landed assets were never returned, but its mission in life was restored by Edward VI. An official extract from the Patent Rolls (translated into more modern English) states:

> In view of the sick and infirm poor men lying begging in the public streets and places of London and its suburbs to the infection and annoyance of the King's subjects using these streets and places: Grant to the mayor and commonalty and citizens of London of the house and site of the late hospital of Thomas Becket in Southwarke, of late called the hospitall of Saynt Thomas in Southwarke, Surr., with the church, steeple, churchyard and all buildings, barns, stables, dove-houses, ponds, yards, orchards, gardens and ground within the said site; also the rectory of Thomas Becket, lately called the parsonage of St. Thomas in Southwarke; the yearly fair [nundinas] in Southwarke which belonged to the said hospitall, and all possessions of the said hospitall in the parish of the said Thomas Becket

The new six-gabled hospital, enlarged here from the panorama, was built in 1507. The first full translation of the Bible was printed by Miles Coverdale in its precincts

also the messuages, land etc. . . . to the yearly value of £154 17s. 1d.

Grant, further, that the said hospitall of Southwarke should in future be the place and house for relieving and sustaining the poor there and shall be called the poorhouse in Southwarke next London of the king's foundation.

The number of people for whom the hospital would have to provide is rather instructive:—

Of ffatherles children	300
Of sore and sick psons	200
Of poore men overburdened with children	350
Of aged persons	400
Of decayed householders	650
Of ydell vagabondes	200

The next duty was to collect money, which they did from the citizens, and "men gave franckly, the worke was so generally well lyked."

17

But over a year elapsed before the hospital was repaired and surgeons appointed. The target was to harbour and receive three hundred inmates, in addition to out-patients. Two hundred and fifty of the aged and diseased were taken into the hospital, but "a nomber of them would watch duely when the porters were absent that they mighte steale oute and falle to their olde occupacon so that a nomber of them were sharply punyshed before they could be brought to abyde within the boundes of their houses." It was, then, Edward VI, himself a permanent invalid, who was responsible for the rehabilitation of St. Thomas's which, bracketed with St. Bartholomew's Hospital, Christ's Hospital and Bridewell, were granted to the City of London as the four Royal Hospitals.

Nothing of note happened to the hospital during the reign of Queen Mary, but the following prescriptions, as practised in those days, are of passing interest:

A medicen for scalde heads:—
Firste take a pynte of Musterd, a pynte of strong Vynegre, a quarter of a lb. of Verdegrease, Two peneworth of oyle de spike, an ounce of peper fynly beaten. Put thereto a handful of sowte [salt]. Boyle them together and styre them well, put in an earthen pote and so use it.

An oyntement to correcte the same yf it fortune to breake oute agayne. Take a lb. of barrow hogges greace well toyed with an handful of goose dunge with whyte ends and as much of shepes dunge, one penesworth of oyle spike, one peneworth of honye, ii oz. dimidium of peper, one oz. of stavesacre [a species of larkspur] and when yt is boyled Then streane it Thoroughe a Clothe. After the fyrst melicyn Take Vynegre warme it and washe it. And so the Scorfe shall be taken Awaye.

The "stews" having been abolished by Henry VIII on his death-bed, the hospital was now being used very largely as a lying-in place for the numerous loose women of Southwark to the exclusion of other patients. It was accordingly declared that no pregnant women were to be admitted, as the hospital was "a house erected for the relief of honest persons and not of harlottes."

By now the patients were enjoying feather beds. Moreover, they were being fed on white bread and could buy beer at a 1d. a quart. Separate wards were also installed, but the threat of Spain seems to have made little or no mark upon the hospital's history, and the hospital minutes were, not surprisingly, more concerned with the building of privies than with world events.

Until the end of 1556 the medical staff consisted only of surgeons, but in the autumn of that year Henry Bull became the first physician of St. Thomas's, for the munificent salary of £13 6s. 8d. per annum. In addition to the qualified staff, lady specialists were often called in. Thus Mother Edwyn undertook, for one mark (13s. 4d.), to heal a boy who was "bursting", but she needed another 1s. for "fustyan" with which to make a truss. She had to return the money if she was not successful in curing this case of hernia.

Amputations were fairly common at this time, and that the patients often survived is shown by the number of payments for wooden legs and crutches

18

In 1553 King Edward VI restored St. Thomas's to London by royal charter "in view of the sick and infirm poor men lying begging in the public streets"

which is recorded. Many of these, no doubt, were seamen who had fought against Spain.

The number of sisters who looked after the patients varied from fifteen to twenty-five. It is regretted that their morals were not much superior to their patients'. Thus, on April 19th, 1563, the matron reported Margaret Allen,

19

a sister, "For that she wolde not do her dutie in her office but ronne to the taverne and neglect her office, wherefore the masters gave her warning to amende hir faulte or elles to leave her service and forther punyshment." On March 8th, 1568: "Yt is ordered that if any of the susters shall disorder themselves by brawlinge one with another, or other misdemeanour, that then upon complaynt made every suche suster to be removed her ward and sustership and discharged the house for ever."

Clearly there must have been a great deal of friction among the sisters at this time or so strongly worded a caution would not have been necessary. Three times is Ann Reader, who was matron from 1572 to 1580, haled before the court for drunkenness, twice she is pardoned on promise of amendment, but on the third occasion is privately dismissed.

Those were the days when whipping posts were common, the French Disease was rife, bulls were baited, and members of the public were hung, drawn and quartered without any stirring of conscience on the part of the public. No wonder that the nurses were scarcely angels of mercy.

The numerous ale-houses of Southwark figure in the domestic records of the fifteenth and sixteenth centuries. Strong beer was a problem to the governors

London, June 24.

Since it hath pleafed God to fuffer this City to be vifited with the *Plague*, it has been the bufinefs of feveral people to report the mortality to be much greater, and the ficknefs to be much more general then God be thanked it is ; whereas *within the walls* of *London* there dyed but 10 of the *Plague* the laft week; There were but 19 *Parifhes* of 130 *Infected*; and very near *two thirds* of the whole number dyed out of *One* of the faid Parifhes; and according to the difcourfe of the City, we hope that in the next Bill there may be fome abatement.

The long series of epidemics which taxed the staff of the Hospital culminated in the Great Plague of 1665. Death holds an hour-glass in this news-sheet

IV

PLAGUE AND FIRE

THE last years of Queen Elizabeth's reign were marked by a bad epidemic of the Plague, which carried off the hospitaller of St. Thomas's as well as its steward. Two years later it is recorded that the back yard of the hospital was in such disrepair that "the poor sometimes get away with things belonging to the hospital and also take in strong beer and disorder themselves." Throughout this and the next century the problem of keeping strong beer out of the hospital was something which the Governors were continually trying to solve.

The hospitallers, who were Chaplains to the Hospital in the early part of the seventeenth century, died like flies, five of them succeeding one another in four years. The post was evidently a dangerous one because the Hospitaller had to interview all urgent applicants for admission and decide whether the sufferer had Plague or not. If he had, he was not as a rule admitted, and the

21

*The Plague was a terrifying visitation on a city ill-equipped to meet it. St. Thomas's staff
remained at their posts, taking charge of plague-stricken soldiers*

hospitaller was the only officer with whom he came into contact. His duties
kept him in the hospital day and night, where he lived in a foul atmosphere
and drank a gallon of beer a day. No wonder the poor man offered little
resistance to disease.

The amount of drugs used in the seventeenth century must have been very
small, as is shown by the appointment of an apothecary in 1621 at £45 a year,
out of which he had to find all the drugs needed in the hospital. In the same
year it is recorded that a surgeon was given a bonus of £10 for "his extraordinary skill in cutting four of his patients for the stone." This is the first
mention of lithotomy in the hospital records, although the operation was
described by Abulkasim in the eleventh century.

In 1627, some one hundred and twenty wounded soldiers were taken to
St. Thomas's and St. Bartholomew's after the disastrous expedition of the
Duke of Buckingham to relieve La Rochelle.

Two years later precautions were again being taken against the Plague by the
Justices of the Peace for Southwark. These consisted of "Apprehending Irish
and vagrants, compiling a list of all alehouses, scouring all the ditches and
providing two watchmen for every infected house." Yet, within another six
years, the hospital had no fewer than two hundred and eighty beds. The names
of the wards were: King's, Queen's, Lydia, Luke, Job, Nightlayers', Jonas,

After the Plague came the Fire. It did not reach St. Thomas's, but much of the Hospital's property in the City was destroyed, with heavy loss of income

Noah, Magdalen, Tobias, Abdiel, Lazarus, Male Foul Ward and Female Foul Ward.

Charles I did not have much to do with the hospital except to suggest candidates for the job of apothecary—who were not accepted. And as soon as was feasible, the hospital espoused the cause of the Parliamentarians. One effect of the Civil War was that the number of civilian patients had to be heavily reduced to make room for wounded soldiers. Sailors, who were casualties in actions against the Dutch, had also to be treated. A new trouble arose in 1655 when several of the hospital sisters became Quakeresses and were promptly discharged.

Ten years later came the Great Plague, when all the wealthier part of the population sought safety in flight. Doctor Wharton, the senior physician, remained in London because Charles II specially asked him to take charge of the plague-stricken soldiers who were brought to St. Thomas's, with a promise of a future reward—never received. Edward Rice, one of the surgeons, who also stuck to his post, was given a bonus of £20 for curing several Army officers.

Then came the Fire of London and, though the hospital itself was spared, much of its city property was burnt to the ground. In view of the loss of income entailed by this, the Governors asked the Admiralty to be relieved of

23

the job of accepting any more wounded sailors. This suggestion was refused, but rules for the Naval patients were drawn up, one of which was "That they take not tobacco in their beds to the indangering of the house by fire."

The first indication of any anatomy school is given by the instruction in 1670, that no surgeon was to dismember the corpse of anyone dying in the hospital on pain of disfavour from the Court of Governors. In 1685 when James II had come to the throne, it was ordered that "the ancient guiacum diet drink and no other is to be given to patients with the foule disease, or French Pox, unless the physicians order other."

A good idea of the Hospital Standing Orders can be gained from a modern translation of some of the minutes of the last meeting of Governors in 1699:

1. No skillet carriers are allowed except at the surgeon's charge.
2. All medicines are to be viewed twice a year by the staff.
3. The hospitaller to visit the poor for their instruction and consolation.
4. The steward, matron, cook and butler to furnish weekly accounts.
5. The butler and cook to serve victuals when the bell rings and the sisters to fetch same.
6. The matron to supervise the sisters and see that they do not lodge outside the hospital.
7. The sisters to see that no card play nor dicing takes place in the house.
8. The sisters to clean their wards by six a.m.
9. The sisters to keep their yards clean and to allow no hens ranging therein.
10. All able patients are to help the sisters.
11. No sister is to use the patients' fuel except for the wards.
12. No patient is to be kept after his presentation.
13. No patient is to be kept to whom no physic or chirurgery is prescribed.
14. The back gate is always to be kept shut except on court days and both gates to be shut at 7 in winter and 8 in summer and opened at 6 in summer and 7 in winter.
15. The sexton is to keep the Chapel and yards clean and to make graves six feet deep, six feet long and three feet wide at eighteen pence each.
16. The officers are to eat their victuals in the house and not to go to alehouses for them.
17. No drink is to be brought in and sold to patients except by the physician's and surgeon's licence.
18. The clothes of dead patients are to be disposed of by the treasurer and two governors (takers in).
19. Every tenth bed is to be left empty to air and not more than one patient is to be put into each bed.
20. Old sheets are to be washed and given to the surgeons for dressings.

21. Neither steward, matron, butler, cook nor porters are to lodge out of the house nor to employ any patient about any but hospital business.

22. No patient with the foul disease shall go out of his ward, nor come into the house to fetch anything, nor within the Chapel, nor sit upon the seats in the courtyards upon pain of expulsion.

23. The porters are not to suffer the poor to go out but upon necessary occasions, and if they return late or drunk they shall be expelled.

24. That such of these orders as govern admitting patients shall be read before the takers in by the steward at each time of admitting.

The mention of these skillet carriers is the first reference to the pupils of what became one of the most famous teaching hospitals in the world. They had the privilege of carrying the surgeon's tray of dressings and instruments and could therefore be close to him while at work.

A physician in the gruesome dress in which
he attended patients during the Plague

*William Cheselden, generally regarded at St.
Thomas's as its greatest surgeon, in the silk turban
which he wore when operating*

V

THE BEGINNINGS OF MODERN MEDICINE

THE advance in Medicine during the seventeenth century had not been very striking compared with the philosophic thought, literature, architecture and scientific research of such men as Bacon, Harvey, Shakespeare, Newton and Wren. However, typhus, enteric and scarlatina were now recognized among the fevers. The virtues of fresh air in sick rooms and wards were understood; Peruvian bark was prescribed for ague; and leprosy, sweating sickness and plague were things of the past.

The arrival of Doctor Richard Mead, as physician for the hospital in 1703, added considerably to the prestige of the hospital. He became the most eminent physician during the reigns of Queen Anne, George I and George II. He was the first to shew that the mortality from measles was due to pneumonia. He attached great importance to post-mortem examinations, and was immortalized by Pope. He was, too, a great friend of Thomas Guy, the bookseller. Guy was a Governor of St. Thomas's and in 1721, from the profit he made out of selling stock in the South Sea Bubble, leased a part of the Hospital's site and built a hospital for taking St. Thomas's incurable and mental cases: at the same time, at Dr. Mead's suggestion, he paid for the building and endowment of three wards in the parent hospital. However, on his death, Guy willed that his hospital should be made open to all types

RICHARDUS . MEAD. M. D.
Regis Magnæ Britanniæ Medicus Ordinarius 1719

*Richard Mead, Physician for St. Thomas's from 1703 to 1714 be-
came a leading figure and the most eminent physician of his time*

of cases and that it should have its own governing body. This latter stipula-
tion inevitably paved the way to the separation of the two hospitals, although
this did not come about as soon as might have been expected and belongs to
another chapter of our story.

During Dr. Mead's reign, lectures on anatomy, with its bearing upon surgery, were given at St. Thomas's, which also had an official dissecting room.
At the same time William Cheselden, who is generally regarded at St.
Thomas's as its greatest surgeon, joined the staff. He specialized in anatomy
and became a leading oculist as well.

A further abstract of the orders of the hospital in 1752 is interesting.

1. That the Steward receive no Person into the House but on Ordinary Court Days, except Accidents, or by Order of the President or Treasurer.

   None received but on court days.

2. Item, That no Person be received, who is visited or suspected to be visited with the Plague, Itch, Scald-Head, or other Infectious Diseases, and if any such be taken in, then to be discharged as soon as discovered.

   None received of Infectious Diseases.

3. Item, That no Person coming from the adjacent parts, shall be admitted without a Certificate from a Church-Warden of the Parish where he or she then lived, or other substantial Person, with a promise to receive them when discharged; and in case of Death, to take away and Bury the Corps, without Charge to this House, except in some extraordinary Cases, to be allowed by the Treasurer or Governors, Takers-in for the time being; and the Steward to take care that the Patients do provide themselves with convenient Linen at their Admittance.

   None received without security.

4. Item, That none put out by Takers-in for the time being be received in again by the succeeding Takers-in, except very likely to be Cured, or have some new Distemper; and the Steward is required to take great care that the new Takers-in be constantly informed of such Person so formerly discharged, when they desire to be taken in again.

   None taken in twice.

5. Item, That none be taken in that in the Opinion of the Doctors and Surgeons are incurable.

   None taken in that are incurable.

6. Item, That no poor Person at their Entrance pay any Money or Gratuity for Garnish or Footing, on Pain of Expulsion of the Person that Demands or Receives it.

   No garnish money.

7. Item, That the Surgeons begin to dress Patients at Nine o'Clock precisely, from Lady-Day to Michaelmas, and at Ten o'Clock precisely from Michaelmas to Lady-Day [a rather significant forerunner of what we now know as British Summer Time]; and that no Doctor, Surgeon, or Apothecary, take any Moneys or Reward for Curing any Poor admitted by the Governors.

   The poor dressed.

28

The second court of St. Thomas's in 1748, with the statue of Edward VI
Oil painting by Samuel Wale

The new front of the hospital in Southwark, completed in 1842

8. Item, That all the Doctors and Surgeons do meet together at the House every Saturday by Eleven of the Clock, and go all together through all the Wards, to visit and inspect the Patients, and then and there jointly Consider and Consult of and concerning such whose Cases are extraordinary and difficult, whether Doctors or Surgeons Patients; and prescribe and direct such Administrations or Operations as shall be by them, or the major Part of them thought fit.

Doctors and Surgeons to meet every Saturday to prescribe.

9. Item, That none be permitted to dress for or under any Surgeons in this House, but such as are bound Apprentices at Surgeon's-Hall, for a Term of seven years at least; and except such Young Surgeons as shall be approved by the Committee of Governors or Treasurer of this House for the time being, according to an Order made at the General-Court, the Seventeenth of March, 1702.

Surgeons Servants.

10. Item, That no Surgeon shall suffer any Servant to perform any Operation, dilate or cut open any Imposthumes, or Sinuous Ulcers, except the Master of such Servant be present, and direct the same. And that no dead Body shall be Opened, Dissected, or Dismembered, without leave from the Treasurer, or Steward in the Absence of the Treasurer.

Surgeons Servants.

11. Item, That some of the Governors, Takers-in for the time being, when they think proper to view the Poor, to see how all Things are managed, and to examine all the Provisions.

Governors to view the poor and provisions.

12. Item, That if any Surgeon have any considerable or extraordinary Operation to perform, he shall give Notice of the time of his doing same to the other Surgeons, that they may be present.

Surgeons to acquaint each other of extraordinary operations.

13. Item, That the Minister or Hospitaller do frequently and carefully visit the Sick and Lame Poor in this House for their Instruction and Consolation, as their Case shall require.

The Ministers duty to visit.

14. Item, That the Patients do constantly attend the Worship of God in the Chapel on Sabbath and other Days, on pain of forfeiting of one Day's Allowance for the first Offence, without reasonable excuse; and upon after Offending, to be punished at discretion of the Treasurer or Steward. And at the time of Ringing the

Patients to go to Chapel.

29

Bell to call to Worship in the Chapel, the Steward take care that the Men Patients, and the Matron the Women Patients, do duly attend the same; and at all other times the Door of the Chapel shall be locked.

15. Item, That all the Money payable on account of Soldiers or other Patients admitted into this Hospital, or for Burials here, be collected by the Steward, and accounted for Monthly.

Stewards account of soldiers' Money.

16. Item, That the Patients shall not Swear or take God's Name in vain, nor revile, or miscall one another, nor strike or beat one another, nor steal Meat or Drink, Apparel, or other thing, one from the other; nor abuse themselves by inordinate Drinking, nor incontinent Living, nor talk, nor act Immodestly, upon pain of Expulsion; and that when they go to or return from their Meals and Beds, they crave God's Blessing, and return Thanks to God. And that a proper Person be appointed to Read at the Desk on Sunday, and on Friday morning to Read in every Ward the Rules and Orders to be observed by the Patients.

No Swearing.

17. Item, That none of the Men go into the Women's Wards, nor the Women into the Men's Wards, without Licence, upon pain of Expulsion.

Men not to go into the Women's wards nor the women into the men's ward.

18. Item, That the Matron take care that the Nurses do their Duty diligently, and that they lodge not out of the House, nor be absent from their Charge, without leave from the Treasurer, or in his Absence the Steward.

Matron's duty.

19. Item, That no Person fetch or carry Fire from one place to another in wooden Vessels, or any other thing which may endanger the Firing of the House.

About fetching Fire.

20. Item, That no Patient sit up in their Wards after Eight of the Clock at Night in Winter, and Nine in Summer, without Licence from the Steward, on pain of Expulsion.

None to sit up late.

21. Item, That no Patient shall stay out of the House after Seven of the Clock at Night in Winter, and Eight in Summer, without special Licence from the Steward, on pain of Expulsion.

No Patient to lye out of the house without Licence.

As for the patient's diet, this was revised and the following scale approved :—

The four new courts of the Hospital in 1758 with the "frontispiece" showing Edward VI and four cripples. Many windows are bricked up after the window tax of 1696

FULL DIET

Breakfast: Milk porridge on four days a week and water gruel on three days.

Dinner: ½ lb. meat on five days a week and 4 ozs. butter or 6 oz. cheese on two days.

Supper: 1 pt. of broth.

Bread: 14 oz. a day. Beer—1 qt. in winter and 3 pints in summer.

MIDDLE OR LOW DIET

Breakfast: As above.

Dinner: 6 oz. mutton or veal on five days a week. Cheese or butter as above on two days.

Supper: As at breakfast.

Bread: 12 oz. a day. Beer—1 qt.

MILK DIET

Breakfast: As above.

Dinner: 1 pt. rice milk on four days a week and 8 oz. pudding on three days.

Supper: As in other diets.

1 qt. of milk and water (⅓ milk) in winter, 3 pints in summer, and 12 oz. of bread daily.

DRY DIET

Breakfast: 2 oz. of cheese or butter.

Dinner: As in full diet.

Supper: As at breakfast.

5 sea biscuits or 14 oz. bread, and 1 qt. of beer a day.

FEVER DIET

Barley water, water gruel, panado (bread boiled in water), thin broth, milk porridge, rice gruel, and balm or sage tea.

VI

THE GROWTH OF THE TEACHING HOSPITAL

By 1800 there were about four hundred and fifty in-patients whose food consisted of meat and cereals in various forms, with milk, butter, cheese and beer. Yet until the beginning of the nineteenth century they never had any fresh vegetables. Potatoes were then added to their diet, but were withdrawn because they were unpopular and bread was preferred. One of the improvements in the hospital was the replacement of candles by oil lamps; gas, of course, was not yet introduced. Admission day was still Thursday, when the physician and surgeon of the week chose the most urgent cases for admission and gave out-patients' cards to others. On Saturdays the medical and surgical officers visited all the wards together and discussed difficult cases. They all had to go into every ward because, at that time, medical and surgical cases were not separated; which explains the reputation of the medical students who accompanied them for "walking the hospital".

These weekly visits, with the consultations involved, must have been most valuable to the pupils who had no handy text-books on medicine and surgery, and were dependent on their lecture notes for their reading. Independent rounds only took place on Tuesdays—a very bad arrangement for the students who were thus prevented from seeing the practice of more than one physician or surgeon each week.

Students were, however, only putting the finishing touches to what they had learnt in a five-year apprenticeship, and the six to eighteen months which they spent in London gave them the opportunity of seeing the latest and most up-to-date treatment of the very serious accidents and diseases which could only have occurred occasionally in a country practice. To the young man of ability the course at St. Thomas's medical school must have been most instructive. For this, he paid £50 a year, the equivalent of at least £250 today; at which period St. Thomas's records shew that the sisters had their salary raised to £32 a year, and nurses to £20 a year; sisters in charge of the Foul Wards received £45 per annum, and the nurses £22 per annum.

At this stage a brief interlude must be introduced. Keats, the poet, was studying medicine at St. Thomas's and his notes are preserved in the Hampstead Public Library to this day. The scene is a room over the tallow chandler's shop in St. Thomas's Street in 1816. Keats is sitting on the window-sill, while Henry Stephens, with whom he lodges, is studying his notes taken that day on medicine.

"I have composed a new line," said the young poet. "A thing of beauty is a constant joy." He turns to Stephens. "What do you think of that?"

"It has the true ring, but is wanting in some way," said Stephens, and went on reading.

Under Sir Astley Cooper the anatomy school reached its heyday. He was a man of great charm and ability, unequalled in his knowledge of human and comparative anatomy

An interval of silence, and then—Keats: "A thing of beauty is a joy for ever."

And thus, in St. Thomas's Street, in dirty sordid Southwark, was born one of the most-quoted lines in English poetry. Stephens, it may be said, was also a stickit doctor. He gave up medicine to invent a new line of ink, which is now a household word. Many years later, Somerset Maugham, another stickit doctor at St. Thomas's, found ink more profitable than medicine.

Curiously enough, no mention is made of vaccination on the hospital records until 1806, although all educated people had accepted it as a safeguard against smallpox by the end of the eighteenth century. Gas, as an illuminant, was not introduced to the hospital until about 1816. In the meantime the anatomy school was in its heyday—largely because Sir Astley Cooper, the lecturer, always managed by means known only to himself to obtain a sufficient supply of bodies for dissection at a reasonable price. Those were the days of the "resurrection men" who sometimes charged as much as £20 for a body, and if they were threatened or beaten down, could stop the supply to a school until the pupils had to drift away elsewhere. Murphy and Crouch, two of the cleverest rascals in the degrading traffic, were at the head of this corporation; but such was their respect for Sir Astley Cooper that the price of a body is said never to have been more than four guineas at St. Thomas's . . .

That the Governors now fully realized their responsibility for medical teaching as well as for the care of the sick is shown by their decision in 1813 to divert three thousand pounds of hospital money to build a department for purely teaching purposes. This building was quite separate from the rest of the hospital.

In those days the pupils of St. Thomas's and Guy's had the right of seeing operations at both hospitals. And, to prevent strangers from invading the small theatres, pupils of the sister hospital were provided with tickets establishing their identity. But this custom of showing tickets had lapsed when one fine day in 1825 St. Thomas's decided that only pupils with tickets would be admitted, which resulted in an actual riot in the St. Thomas's hospital theatre. The police were called and six medical students were arrested, thus snapping the last link between St. Thomas's and Guy's. It also led to a very considerable deterioration in St. Thomas's medical school. Dreary and inefficient lecturers were responsible for the decline in attendance until the numbers dropped to a miserable thirty-four.

In 1838 the report of the "Commissioners Concerning Charities" was published, nearly a hundred pages of which dealt with St. Thomas's. Each of the full physicians received £40 a year from the hospital, and the average fees for pupils, for ten years, came to £199 a year; in addition to which the physician received fees for the lectures he gave. The full surgeons were better paid, because their average receipts for pupils came to £248 a year and the commissioners do not seem to have considered the apprentices, each of whom paid a lump sum of five hundred guineas.

With regard to the patients, it is recorded that in 1836 thirty-six had been discharged for ill-conduct, mostly from the male foul wards. It is also reported that the matron at that time was trying to get a better class of sisters than was possible under the old system of promoting nurses. The nurses' duties were onerous and disagreeable, the stipends low, and frequent changes were necessary. The hospitaller read prayers in the chapel every morning at 9.30 and held an evening service, with a sermon, on Sunday afternoon. He visited the wards every morning. Roman Catholic and Jewish ministers were allowed to attend when required, but dissenting ministers were excluded because they "excited the patients".

On operating days all three surgeons attended. The physicians and surgeons went their rounds at 1 p.m., their visit lasting about an hour and a half. The apothecary went round at 10.30 each morning and prescribed for medical and, if necessary, surgical patients; he was still the resident medical officer except where surgical operation was needed. Though Pathology was making headway (for, in 1836, 147 post-mortem examinations were made) the minutes of the lecturers who met eight or ten times a year make very depressing reading. At more than half the meetings there were complaints, accusations, or threats of resignation. They had not even the self-respect to keep their grievances to their own body; and on more than one occasion disparaged one another to the students.

On October 1st, 1847, a residential "Collegiate Establishment" was instituted. Bedrooms and sitting-rooms were to be had at 4, 5 and 6 Dean Street, and an entrance fee of two guineas was charged. For 30/- a week, paid in advance, a student had a bedroom and a half-share in a sitting-room with breakfast at 8 a.m., lunch from 12 noon to 1 p.m., tea at 5 p.m. and dinner from 8 p.m. to 9 p.m. He had to be in by midnight, at which hour all guests had to leave. But in the next four years only twenty-one students seem to have occupied the rooms. Probably the fees charged were too high and the number of students too small to make it a success.

In December 1844 the first Royal governor of the hospital was appointed in the person of Albert, Prince Consort. In earlier times monarchs had spoken of "This our hospital of St. Thomas", but Edward VI was the only one who had ever helped it in any way until now. Accordingly, a deputation, consisting of the president, treasurer, two governors and the clerk, went to Windsor Castle on January 8th, 1845, and presented the Prince with the customary green staff. The numbering of Prince Albert among the governors was followed on June 26th, 1845, by his giving away the prizes to successful students at St. Thomas's.

In August 1847 house surgeons were appointed for the first time. Candidates were to hold the qualifications of M.R.C.S., L.S.A., and old St. Thomas's students were to be preferred. Two of them were to replace the resident assistant surgeon, who now ceased to be resident.

In 1847 schemes for the extension of the railway line from Hungerford Bridge to Charing Cross started to assume threatening aspects as it was patently clear that St. Thomas's occupied a site which such a line must inevitably traverse.

At the time the prospect of ejection was viewed with grave anxiety and some believed that a calamity of this magnitude would be the death-knell of St. Thomas's. When the Charing Cross Railway scheme became law and the Hospital was compulsorily bought out for £296,000, none could have foreseen how rich a blessing was masquerading in the guise of tragedy.

Visiting day in 1871, in the temporary quarters found in the animal houses of the Surrey Gardens during the Hospital's removal from Southwark

Various sites were inspected before the present position was bought for £100,000. But a temporary abode had to be found for some, at least, of the patients until the new hospital could be ready. Strangely enough, the most suitable premises were the Surrey Gardens with their giraffe house and lion cages, their pavilion and music hall. The music hall was divided into three floors so as to hold two hundred beds; the giraffe house was used as a cholera ward; the pavilion became a chemical laboratory; and the elephant house was converted into a dissecting room.

In the meantime, the Crimean War had been fought and the name of Florence Nightingale* had become a household word.

---

* In 1856, shortly after the Peace of Paris, a dinner was given to the Naval and Military Officers who had served in the Crimean War. After dinner it was suggested that each guest should write down the name of the person whose service would, in his opinion, be longest remembered by posterity. The papers were examined, and each one bore the same name — Florence Nightingale.

VII

THE VISION OF MISS NIGHTINGALE

THREE people contributed more than anybody else to the relief of human suffering in the nineteenth century:—Simpson, who introduced chloroform; Lister, who invented antiseptic surgery; and Florence Nightingale, the founder of modern nursing. But the third development would still have been invaluable, even if the use of anæsthetics and antiseptics had not been discovered.

Nursing by women is as old as Christianity, and for centuries the religious orders sent cultivated women into the hospitals; the very name of "sister" recalls its historically religious origin. There was nothing novel, therefore, in Florence Nightingale's service as a war nurse except that she was English. Sisters had already accompanied armies of other countries to the field. But in England the objections to any kind of nursing by gentlewomen were almost immovable. It was felt that they would be exposed, if not to danger and temptations, at least to undesirable conditions.

"It was as if I had wanted to be a kitchen maid," Florence Nightingale recalled many years later when she spoke of her early wishes to become a nurse.

The idea was widely prevalent that for most cases in hospital practice a modest woman was, from the nature of things, unsuited to act as a nurse. Even as late as the middle of the last century a doctor was quoted as saying that hospitals always engaged nurses "without any character, as no responsible person would undertake so disagreeable an office. The duties they have to perform are most unpleasant and it is little wonder that many of them drink, as they require something to keep up the stimulus." The ordinary wages were £14–£16 a year. Moreover, they had no uniform dress, cooked their own food (which they bought themselves) and ate their meals in the ward kitchens or scullery. Most of them were rough, unobservant and untaught. No high standard of efficiency was expected; no training was organized; and it was generally regarded as a menial occupation which did not attract women of character. They had to pick up their knowledge in the wards. "A poor woman is left a widow with two or three children," wrote *The Times* of the day. "What is she to do? She would starve on needlework; she is unfit for domestic service; she knows nobody to give her charring; and she has no money to buy a mangle. So she gets a recommendation from a clergyman and is engaged as a hospital nurse."

No wonder that Mr. Nightingale, a wealthy Derbyshire land-owner, did everything to dissuade his daughter from becoming a nurse. Rather as if she were a flighty girl who needed to be separated from an undesirable suitor, he kept on sending her abroad; but on each visit she fell more in love with the

Florence Nightingale, whose zeal and revolutionary vision established the tradition of modern nursing. It sprang from her training school at St. Thomas's

idea of nursing. First at the Kaiserswerth Hospital in Germany, and secondly at the Maison de la Providence, belonging to the Sisters of Charity in Paris, Miss Nightingale began to acquire a real knowledge of practical nursing. When the Crimean War broke out, she was thirty-four years old and was most impressed by the famous dispatches of Russell, the *Times* war correspondent, who revealed the deplorable conditions in the army hospitals out there. Promptly she wrote to a friend at the War Office offering her services.

Mr. Sidney Herbert, who had met her previously, had already written to her asking if she would like to go out. The letters crossed and in a few days' time she set off to Scutari with a party of thirty-eight nurses and sisters. One of these was Mrs. Roberts from St. Thomas's, whom Miss Nightingale described in a letter as "worth her weight in gold", as opposed to some others whom she described as "not being fit to take care even of themselves".

There is no need to recapitulate Miss Nightingale's magnificent work in the Crimea. Suffice it to say that as a result of the wonderful work she did the public gratefully subscribed £50,000 to a fund which she would supervise.

As a result of her published observations and comments on the way to improve nursing, civil as well as military, she had already made close contact with the officials of hospitals up and down the country. Among them was Mr. Whitfield, the resident medical officer of St. Thomas's at the time of the compulsory move from Southwark to the Albert Embankment. Miss Nightingale was approached by Mr. Whitfield in his predicament and threw herself wholeheartedly into the matter. Mr. Whitfield had from the first been in favour of compelling the railway company to buy all the hospital's land, or none at all, so that in the former event the hospital would be re-built on a healthier site and on an improved plan. Miss Nightingale agreed with him entirely and among other things wrote a strong letter to the Prince Consort, with the result that the governors decided to do as she suggested.

It was, indeed, a fortunate coincidence that the removal of St. Thomas's from Southwark and the need to build a brand-new hospital should have synchronized with Miss Nightingale's ability to draw on the £50,000 Nightingale Fund as she chose. Luckily, too, for St. Thomas's, she had met Mrs. Wardroper in 1854 when the expedition of nurses was sent to the Crimean War, and Mrs. Wardroper was a woman after her own heart; strong, devoted to her work and, as Miss Nightingale herself described her "straightforward, true, upright and decided. . . . She was free from selfishness. Her whole heart and mind; her whole life and strength were in the work she had undertaken. Her force of character was extraordinary. Her word was law. She was a thorough gentlewoman, nothing low or mean about her."

After much consultation with Mrs. Wardroper and Mr. Whitfield Miss Nightingale formulated her historic scheme for the foundation of the Nightingale School. The basis of the agreement was that St. Thomas's was to provide the facility for the training and the Nightingale Fund was to pay the cost and the payment of the nurses themselves. In May 1860, advertisements were inserted in the public Press inviting candidates for admission, and in less than two months fifteen probationers were admitted for a year's training. It was, therefore, a modest school, but planned with a vast amount of forethought, through which the scheme destined to found the modern art and practice of nursing was finally launched. A rare copy of the first report of the Committee of the Council of the Nightingale Fund shows that the following regulations were laid down as to the admission and training of the probationers :—

Florence Nightingale, aged nineteen (seated), with her sister
Water-colour by W. White

The hospital at Scutari: Florence Nightingale visiting the wards

1. The Committee of the Nightingale Fund have made arrangements with the authorities of St. Thomas's Hospital for giving a year's training to women desirous of working as Hospital Nurses.
2. Women desirous of receiving this course of training should apply to Mrs. Wardroper, the Matron, at St. Thomas's Hospital, subject to whose selection they will be received into the Hospital as Probationers. The age considered desirable for Probationers is from 25 to 35; a certificate of age and a testimonial of character, according to a form which will be supplied by Mrs. Wardroper, will be required, also the name and address of medical attendant.
3. The Probationers will be under the authority of the Matron of the Hospital, and will be subject to the rules of the Hospital.
4. They will be supplied at the cost of the Nightingale Fund, with separate lodging in the Hospital and with board, including tea and sugar, and with their washing; and they will be furnished with a certain quantity of outer clothing. They will serve as assistant-nurses in the wards of the Hospital.
5. They will receive instruction from the Sisters and the Resident Medical Officer. They will be paid, at the end of the first quarter, a sum of £2; at the end of the second quarter, £2 10s.; at the end of the third quarter, £2 10s.; and at the end of the fourth quarter, £3.
6. At the close of a year, their training will be considered complete, and they will be expected to enter into service as Hospital Nurses in such situations as may be offered to them.
7. The names of the Probationers will be entered in a Register, in which a record will be kept of their conduct and qualifications. This will be submitted at the end of every month to the Committee of the Nightingale Fund. At the end of a year those whom the Committee find to have passed satisfactorily through the course of instruction and training, will be entered in the Register as certificated Nurses, and will be recommended for employment accordingly.
8. The term of a Probationer's service is a complete year, and they will be received on the distinct understanding that they will remain for that length of time. They may, however, be allowed to withdraw upon grounds to be approved by the Committee, upon three months' notice. They will be subject to be discharged at any time by the Matron, in case of misconduct, or should she consider them inefficient or negligent of their duties. They will be eligible, upon proof of competency, during their year of training, or at its close, to permanent appointments as extra nurses in St. Thomas's Hospital. The Committee look forward with confidence to being able to find situations for their certificated Nurses, either in St. Thomas's or some other Hospital.
9. The Committee will allow gratuities of £5 and £3, according to two classes of efficiency, to all their certificated Nurses, on receiving evidence of their having served satisfactorily in a Hospital during one entire year succeeding that of their training.

Of the original fifteen probationers, three were dismissed during the course of the year; one retired owing to ill-health; and two were appointed as extra nurses in St. Thomas's Hospital. The six vacancies were filled by additional probationers, one of whom was dismissed. Thirteen, including the two extra nurses, completed their year's course. Of these, four were received into the hospital; one was appointed nurse to the union workhouse at Stockton-on-Tees; one to the union workhouse at Warrington; three returned to their homes; while applications were under consideration for placing two others. Eleven were placed on the register of certificated nurses, seven in the first class and four in the second. The course of training given to the probationers was almost exclusively of a practical kind, and the details of the qualifications expected of them were contained in the following memorandum :—

You are required to be:—
> SOBER,
> HONEST,
> TRUTHFUL,
> TRUSTWORTHY,
> PUNCTUAL,
> QUIET AND ORDERLY,
> CLEANLY AND NEAT.

You are expected to become skilful :—
1. In the dressing of blisters, burns, sores, wounds, and in applying fomentations, poultices, and minor dressings.
2. In the application of leeches, externally and internally.
3. In the administration of enemas for men and women.
4. In the management of trusses, and appliances in uterine complaints.
5. In the best method of friction to the body and extremities.
6. In the management of helpless Patients, i.e., moving, changing, personal cleanliness of, feeding, keeping warm (or cool), preventing and dressing bed sores, managing position of.
7. In bandaging, making bandages, and rollers, lining of splints, &c.
8. In making the beds of the Patients, and removal of sheets whilst Patient is in bed.
9. You are required to attend at operations.
10. To be competent to cook gruel, arrowroot, egg flip, puddings, drinks, for the sick.
11. To understand ventilation, keeping the Ward fresh by night as well as by day; you are to be careful that great cleanliness is observed in all the utensils; those used for the secretions as well as those required for cooking.
12. To make strict observation of the sick in the following particulars :— The state of secretions, expectoration, pulse, skin, appetite; intelligence, as delirium or stupor; breathing, sleep, state of wounds, eruptions, formation of matter, effect of diet or of stimulants, and of medicines.
13. And to learn the management of convalescents.

The essential principles of the scheme were stated by Miss Nightingale to be twofold: "1. That nurses should have their technical training in hospitals specially organized for the purpose; 2. That they should live in a home fit to form their moral life and discipline." The scheme was carefully adjusted to these two ends. The pupils served as assistant nurses in the wards of the Hospital. They received instruction from the sisters and the resident medical officer. Other members of the medical staff—Dr. Bernays, Dr. Brinton, and Mr. Le Gros Clark—gave lectures.

How seriously the pupils were expected to undertake their studies, how strictly their superiors would watch their progress, is shown by the formidable "Monthly Sheet of Personal Character and Acquirements of each Nurse" which Miss Nightingale drew up for the Matron to fill in. The Moral Record was under five heads: punctuality, quietness, trustworthiness, personal neatness and cleanliness, and ward management. The Technical record was under fourteen main heads, some of them with as many as ten or twelve sub-heads: "observation of the sick" was especially detailed in this manner. Against each item of personal character or technical acquirement, the nurse's record was to be marked as Excellent, Good, Moderate, Imperfect, or 0. Those who "passed the examiners", as it were, at the end of their year's course, were placed on the Hospital Register as Certificated Nurses. Decidedly Miss Nightingale emphasized the educational side of her new experiment. No public school, university, nor other institution ever had so elaborate and exhaustive a system of marks. Equally thorough and scientific were the "General Directions" which the resident medical officer presently drew up at Miss Nightingale's earnest request "For the Training of the Probationer Nurses in taking Notes of the Medical and Surgical Cases in Hospitals".

Equal care was taken to ensure Miss Nightingale's second principle. The Hospital was to be a home as well as a school. The upper floor of a new wing of St. Thomas's Hospital was fitted up for the accommodation of the pupils, so as to provide a separate bedroom for each, a common sitting-room, and two rooms for the sister in charge of them. No pupil was admitted without a testimonial of good character. Their board, lodging, washing and uniform were provided by the Fund. They were given £10 for their personal expenses. The chaplain addressed them twice a week. They were placed under the direct authority of the Matron, whose discipline (as will have been gathered from Miss Nightingale's character-sketch) was strict. The least flightiness was reprimanded, and any pronounced flirtation was visited with the last penalty. "Although", wrote the Matron to Miss Nightingale, with regard to one probationer, "I have not the smallest reason to doubt the correctness of her moral character, her manner, nevertheless, is objectionable, and she uses her eyes unpleasantly; as her years increase, this failing—an unfortunate one—may possibly decrease." A girl who was detected in daily correspondence, and in "walking out" with a medical student was dismissed. The nurses were only allowed to go out two together. "Of course, we parted as soon as we got to the corner," said one of them later.

When the probationers had finished their training, they were expected to enter into service as hospital nurses, or in such other situations in public institutions as might be offered to them. It was not intended that they should enter upon private nursing. This was an important point in Miss Nightingale's scheme. She had it in her mind from the first that her Training School should in its turn be the means of training elsewhere. She wanted to sow an acorn which might in course of time produce a forest.

In these days, when all our great hospitals have their training schools for nurses, when the tendency is towards increasing the requirements beyond the standard described in this chapter, and when nursing has become a highly organized profession, it requires some effort to realize how novel, and even how daring, was the work of the founder of modern nursing. Just as a certain crusty colonel of the old school has naïvely helped to explain the difficulties of Miss Nightingale's experiment in the Crimean War, so a surgeon of the old school wrote a little book which is invaluable in helping us to realize the novelty of her experiment in St. Thomas's Hospital. He was of the highest distinction in his profession; Hunterian Orator and twice President of the College of Surgeons. He was also senior surgeon at St. Thomas's Hospital, a fact which perhaps explains Mrs. Wardroper's anticipation of "rather harsh criticism"; for Mr. South was strongly and even bitterly opposed to the whole idea of the Nightingale Fund, and of any new provision for the training of nurses. He was "not at all disposed to allow that the nursing establishments of our hospitals are inefficient, or that they are likely to be improved by any special institution for training." He believed that the nursing at St. Thomas's was good (as indeed in many respects it was), and he did not perceive that what the Nightingale Fund had in view was to raise the general level, and to send out from St. Thomas's trained nurses, who in their turn would train other nurses elsewhere. Perhaps, even if he had realized this, he would have regarded it as superfluous. His point of view was that of the man who finds the world very well as it is.

Miss Nightingale's carriage in the Crimea. Preserved in the Hospital, it was damaged by blast from a bomb and is now restored

44

VIII

THE VISION FULFILLED: THE NIGHTINGALE NURSES

IN spite of this hostility from so many quarters, a satisfactory number of Nightingale probationers who had been trained at St. Thomas's Hospital were appointed to important posts in various parts of the country. Within four years two had become lady superintendents, four had been made matrons, one a superintendent and another a sister.

By 1865 the applications from other hospitals for trained St. Thomas's nurses was overwhelming. The institutions supplied with certified nurses in the next few months included the Manchester Nurses' Training Institution; Dorset County Hospital; the Royal Infirmary, Margate; Addenbrooke's Hospital, Cambridge; Swansea Infirmary; Cardiff Infirmary; and the Derbyshire General Infirmary at Derby.

But at the instigation of Miss Nightingale the Committee of her Training School at St. Thomas's refused to send out nurses in driblets to any given hospital. Instead, they strictly adhered to the practice of supplying a complete staff of nurses to take charge of the wards with, if possible, a superintendent. Nor were the applications for St. Thomas's nurses confined to Great Britain. One probationer from the Nightingale School was appointed matron of the hospital at Upsala in Sweden. Another became Lady Superintendent of the Sydney Infirmary, New South Wales, which had applied through the Government of New South Wales for not only a trained superintendent, but also for a staff of head nurses who could establish a training school on the spot.

Nearer home two contingents of nurses, headed by Miss Agnes Jones, were sent to the Liverpool Infirmary. Miss Jones became Lady Superintendent and in a short while over a thousand patients came directly under her supervision. By this time the demand for superintendents, matrons and sisters was so great that the Committee of the Nightingale Fund found it necessary to announce that they desired to emphasize still further their invitation to suitable candidates for admission to the School with a view to their qualifying for "superior situations". They also had to point out that the Nightingale School was solely a training school for nurses and not a medical school for women.

Next year (1866) a new agreement of the Nightingale Committee was made with St. Thomas's whereby the hospital undertook to accommodate thirty-eight probationers, on condition that no similar arrangements with other hospitals were made. To provide for this the "Nightingale Home" was planned for the new hospital which was to contain 569 beds. It says much for Miss Nightingale that her school was so successful during this phase, although the new hospital had not yet been completed, and the old one had been dismantled.

Then at last the great day dawned—June 21st, 1871. Queen Victoria arrived from Windsor at noon, accompanied by several members of the Royal Family, and declared the hospital open—three years after she had laid the foundation stone.

Patients began to arrive, but very slowly. There were only ten transferred from the old Surrey Gardens quarters, and it took some time for the sick poor of Lambeth to realize that a new healer had come among them, although the great new hospital, facing the Houses of Parliament, was welcomed in the most glowing terms by the Press.

Nursing at the new hospital was immensely improved by the employment of all available Nightingale probationers. Fourteen were made nurses and six

On 21st June 1871 the great new Hospital facing the Houses of Parliament wa

became sisters, so the wards were soon staffed by properly trained women, who were being continually kept up to the mark by Miss Nightingale herself. She now took charge not only of the technical, but also of the moral education of her probationers. She had already observed that some of them appointed to responsible posts were not always adequate to their duties. Sometimes their technical education did not reach the high standard on which she insisted. Sometimes she felt that the moral standard was falling short of her ideal, and that nursing was now being regarded more as a business profession and less as a sacred calling. She began to insist on Bible classes and hymn singing. In order to maintain the flow of particularly high-minded probationers, she even applied to Spurgeon, the famous preacher, to procure her candidates

pened by Queen Victoria. She had laid the foundation stone three years before

47

Nursing is become a profession. Trained Nursing no longer an object but a fact. But, oh, if home Nursing could become an every day fact here in this big city of London, the biggest in the world, in an island the smallest inhabited island in the world. But here in London in feeding — a most important branch of it — if you ask a mother who has perhaps brought you a sick

child to "look at": "What have you given it to eat?" She answers triumphantly, "O, it has the same as we have" (!). Yes, often including the gin. And a city where milk, & good milk, is now easier to get than in the country. For all farmers send their milk to London or the great cities. A sick child has been sent to Hospital (and recovered). You ask what it had: "O, they gave it nothing — nothing —

From the "Mother-chief" to her "children": extracts from a letter written on 28th May 1900

from his congregation. But in her desire to stress the religious side of nursing, Miss Nightingale did not allow herself to forget the importance of securing as many responsible and remunerative appointments for her probationers as possible all over the country. Very soon hospitals, workhouses and infirmaries everywhere looked to the Nightingale School of St. Thomas's for superintendents. Sometimes, if an important post was advertised, Miss Nightingale used her own influence to secure the election of a St. Thomas's probationer.

By 1882, former Nightingale probationers held the post of matron or of superintendent of nurses in the following institutions:—Cumberland Infirmary (Carlisle), Edinburgh Royal Infirmary, Huntingdon County Hospital, Leeds Infirmary, Lincoln County Hospital; at Liverpool, in the Royal Infirmary, the Southern Hospital and the Workhouse Infirmary; Netley, Royal Victoria Hospital; Putney, Royal Hospital for Incurables; Salisbury Infirmary; Sydney (N.S.W.) General Hospital; at Marylebone Workhouse Infirmary, the Metropolitan and National Nursing Association, the North London District Nursing Association, the Paddington Association, St. Mary's Hospital, and the Westminster Hospital.

To many of these Institutions a large number of nurses, forming in some cases a complete nursing staff, had been provided from the Nightingale School, and the result was the gradual introduction into British hospitals of

prophecy has been!
Woman was the drudge
Now she is the teacher.
Let her not forfeit it
by being the arrogant,
the "Equal with Men".
She does not forfeit it
by being the "help" "meet".

Now, will you let me
try to thank you,
tho' words cannot
express my thankfulness,
for all your kind thoughts,
for your beautiful Book,

& basket of flowers
& kind wishes, all.
God bless you all
and me your mother chief
as you are good enough
to call me,
my dear children
Florence Nightingale

To
all our Nurses

Florence Nightingale wrote this characteristic letter to her nurses when she was eighty

an organized system of trained nursing. "Nightingale Nurses" also became matrons or superintendents in many Colonies, in India, in Sweden, in Germany, and in the United States. Moreover, other hospitals and institutions followed the lead of Miss Nightingale and established training schools, several of which were also superintended by her pupils; as, for instance, at Edinburgh (under Miss Pringle), at the Marylebone Infirmary (Miss Vincent), at St. Mary's (Miss Williams), and at the Westminster (Miss Pyne).

These schools in their turn sent out lady superintendents, matrons, and nurses to other institutions, and thus the movement of the waters, which Miss Nightingale was able to start after her return from the Crimea, extended in an ever-widening circle. "Let us hail", she said in an address to her own probationers (1884), "the successes of other Training Schools, sprung up, thank God, so fast and well in latter years. But the best way we can hail them is not to be left behind ourselves. Let us, in the spirit of friendly rivalry, rejoice in their progress, as they do, I am sure, in ours. ALL can win the prize. One training school is not lowered because others win. On the contrary, all are lowered if others fail."

In 1879 a memorandum entitled "Directions to Ward Sisters on Instruction to Probationers" was drawn up to improve the ward teaching. "Every new probationer is to be taught . . . how to dust the ward, the screens and their inside ledges; the chairs, etc. . . . how to do dressings using two basins for washing wounds; and never dripping soiled tow or cotton wool into basin No. 1." Besides recalling procedures, the Memorandum constantly reminded the sisters that "the probationer cannot be made responsible for doing well what she does not know how to do."

It was also part of the sisters' duty to fill in a confidential report on each probationer's progress and conduct. Here is the original version.

SISTER

NAME OF PROBATIONER
WARD   Date
NATURE OF DUTY

	Remarks
Punctual	
Quiet	
Trustworthy	
Personally Neat and Clean ..	
Ward Management	
Dressings .. .'. ..	
Enemas	
Catheters	
Helpless Patients	
Bandaging	
Making ditto	
Making Beds	
Waiting on Operations	
Preparing Patient for Operation..	
Sick Cooking	
Keeping Wards fresh	
Cleanliness of Utensils	
Management of Convalescents ..	
Observations on the Sick ..	

Unfortunately, the Medical Students' School at St. Thomas's had not at first kept pace with the progress of the training of probationer nurses there. The number of candidates was painfully small and barely justified the maintenance of the Medical School and its lecturers' fees. The appointment, however, of Dr. Charles Murchison as full physician to the hospital in its new surroundings had an immediate effect. He was probably the greatest clinical teacher of medicine in London and for nine years he seldom went round the wards with a class of less than fifty or sixty students. His method of teaching was exactly what men with examinations to face needed— tabulated, definite, and carried on by viva voce examination.

Other distinguished doctors and surgeons on the staff at St. Thomas's were Mr. Sydney Jones, Doctor Stone and Doctor Bristowe. But all three, as well as Doctor Bernays, Doctor Taylor and Doctor Copeman had retired by 1892, by which stage the number of first-year medical students had dropped

A lecture in chemistry, 1886. The Medical School, developing more slowly than the Nightingale School, was nevertheless a characteristic and integral part of the Hospital's work

to the pitiful total of forty-three. By contrast over 1,500 applications were received in a single year for thirty-two vacancies among the probationers.

In the meantime, Florence Nightingale introduced the innovation of sending her probationers to the National Training School of Cookery, and then looked over their notes on the lessons. She also spent three or four hours alone with each of her fully trained nurses before they began work in the various infirmaries which applied for them. "Yesterday," she wrote to one of her close friends, "we opened the new Marylebone Infirmary (760 beds). We nurse it entirely with our own trained nurses, thank God."

In 1891 the Medical School block was built, together with extra classrooms and a students' club. Another attraction was the first appearance of the *St. Thomas's Hospital Gazette*, which kept old students in touch with the hospital. Not long after its launching (May 1896), the *Gazette* was able to describe an historic occasion at St. Thomas's. Under the report of the Medical and Physical Society, given here with comments which appeared in the *Gazette* for February, 1944, will be found:

"At a meeting of the Medical and Physical Society held on Thursday evening, February 13th, Dr. Mackenzie in the Chair, a demonstration of photography by means of Professor Röntgen's newly discovered x-rays was given in the new Club smoking room of the hospital. We may perhaps be permitted to congratulate ourselves on having had in St. Thomas's 'the first practical demonstration in a London hospital of the Röntgen rays in photographing the interior of a living subject' (*vide* daily press).

"Mr. Stanley Kent, who conducted the demonstration, briefly described the original discovery of Professor Röntgen and its application to the photography of the bony skeleton of living patients . . ." After a brief description of the method of production of the X-rays, samples of X-ray tubes were shewn and a demonstration of the new method was given, one of the objects selected being a hand exhibiting an old fracture of one of the fingers. "Since the above demonstration, Mr. Stanley Kent has been able, by means of improved apparatus, greatly to simplify the process, and to obtain photographs of deeply seated organs of the body, the spine, showing details of vertebrae, the pelvic bones, etc. These advances have been chiefly due to the introduction of a new form of Crookes's tube (known as the 'focus' tube) designed by Mr. Jackson, of King's College, and manufactured by Mr. Müller. So greatly superior to the old form is this tube, that cases which it was formerly impossible to photograph in half an hour, are now easily accomplished in five minutes, and cases which before were impossible are now undertaken with confidence."

Recently there has come into the possession of the X-ray Department what is thought to be the print of this first X-ray of the hand taken in the Hospital, sent by a St. Thomas's doctor who, as a student, was the subject of this first practical demonstration in a London hospital of the Röntgen rays. Although badly faded, it is still possible from this old print to detect the appearance of an old fracture of the head and neck of the fifth metacarpal bone. It is interesting to think that such an early start was made in the use of the newly found X-rays and that St. Thomas's Hospital was the first to stage a demonstration of the method.

In 1897, the first full working year of the Department, a total of 416 cases was X-rayed, 262 males and 154 females, of whom 114 were in-patients.
In 1908 the total number of patients going through the department was 797, and this grew to 1,253 in 1909.
It was not until 1912 that fully protected radiography was used as routine and proper screening apparatus was installed.
In the year 1938-39 the approximate turnover of patients on the diagnostic side of the department was about 28,000.

Towards the close of the century a number of improvements were made to the hospital building. Plans were prepared for four new operating theatres in place of the two old ones, together with two children's wards. The Casualty Department was also re-modelled at a cost of several thousand pounds.

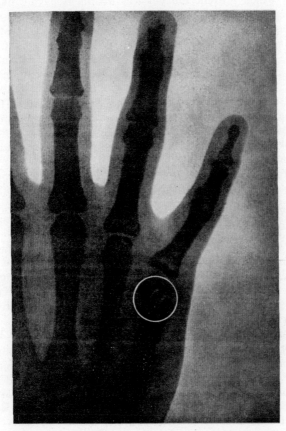

The first X-ray photograph to be taken in a London hospital.
It revealed an old fracture in a student's fifth finger

53

IX

NEW STANDARDS, NEW KNOWLEDGE:
THE TWENTIETH CENTURY

W ITH the vast strides in applied medicine between the start of the twentieth century and World War II grew a realization that treatment did not end with the nurse, nor responsibility on the discharge of the patient. This consciousness of a need for rehabilitation and follow-up work resulted, in 1905, in the establishment of a Lady Almoner's Department. Today, there are two dozen assistant lady almoners who do all they can to remove those troubles and anxieties which prevent the physical treatment having its full effect. They also keep in touch with special cases in their own homes.

Long before the phrase "social medicine" became almost universal, St. Thomas's stressed the fact that only by the closest co-operation between the almoners, doctors and nurses could the welfare of the patient be secure. Maternity and child welfare, probably the most important public health movement of the twentieth century, was pioneered by St. Thomas's. The conditions in which babies were born in the slum area around the hospital were shocking. Seldom was any preparation made for the care of the baby after it was born. St. Thomas's was the first hospital to realize that mothers ought to book with the hospital when early in pregnancy instead of sending for the doctor at the last moment.

As a result of this it also became possible to insist on a proper standard of decency and preparedness in the homes of the expectant mothers. These requirements were regarded as revolutionary and caused great resentment among the inhabitants of Lambeth. But systematic home-visiting produced good results.

Pioneering work was also undertaken by St. Thomas's in connection with the social care of tuberculous patients. A trained almoner was appointed to the chest department and an evening clinic was established so that working-class sufferers could attend without loss of time and pay. The recognition of phthisis as a social disease was very slow, and in those days sanatorium treatment was not provided by the State as a matter of right.

At least four years before Florence Nightingale's death in 1910, her original Home was proved to be quite inadequate to house the existing staff and students. A new building known as Gassiot House was therefore built for them. Later on two extra storeys were added to the original Nightingale Home. Still later the late Lady Riddell, who had herself trained in the Nightingale School, gave £100,000 for the construction of a home which would provide club and recreational facilities as well as relieve the strain on the ordinary accommodation of the nurses. This provided for one hundred and sixty-five of the nursing staff, as well as a swimming pool.

The present nurses home, bungalow's
I saw the living room, lounges &
mementos of F. Nightingale's
also the swimming pool

*To provide accommodation for the School of Nursing, the Nightingale Home
was planned as part of the Hospital. It was destroyed by enemy action in 1941*

In the meantime, the Medical School had at last begun to attract candidates
on relatively as large a scale as the Nightingale School. The numbers of medical students doubled and doubled again, until it was finally necessary to build
St. Thomas's House on the east side of Lambeth Palace Road to provide
further accommodation for the medical students, together with club and
recreational facilities.

As knowledge progressed, and specialization in every aspect of medicine
became the order of the day, orthopædic surgery was introduced and dietetics
were studied with such seriousness that the whole dietary system of the
hospital was revised.

The dispensary, the X-ray and physiotherapy departments were
modernized; post-natal and ante-natal clinics were re-equipped for the
mothercraft department; and the Out-Patients' Department, with an annual
aggregate of 60,000 attendances, was also brought up to date.

Massage represents yet another of the ancillary services to suffering
humanity in the development of which St. Thomas's played a pioneer role.

Already in 1911 two Swedish gymnasts were treating both men and women patients under the general direction of a competent medical officer. Unfortunately, however, when war broke out in 1914, the two Swedes left, and their work was delegated to two porters. . . .

Because members of the staff experienced some difficulty in getting their ward patients treated by the nursing staff (who received twelve lessons in massage for this purpose) the governors decided to establish a training school. This began with one sister and two students who were prepared for the examination of the Chartered Society of Massage and Medical Gymnastics. Physiology lectures were given in conjunction with the nurses and the School grew rapidly. The massage course was later extended from three to six months, and that in medical gymnastics from four to six months.

Meanwhile considerable interest was being aroused in ultra-violet ray treatment, and a small room was built for its research by the governors. In 1915 an examination in medical electricity was instituted, which was the forerunner of what became a Department of Electrotherapy, incorporating ultra-violet, infra-red ray and short-wave treatment.

The Massage School today, embracing as it does both the Physiotherapy and Electrotherapy sections, comes under the ægis of the Matron.

Most of the other large hospitals have imitated the St. Thomas's scheme almost exactly when setting up their own schools of physical medicine. But it is only in recent years that physiotherapy has at last caught the imagination of the Government and public. Industrial and social medicine, rehabilitation and occupational therapy all enter into it.

All these improvements cost hundreds of thousands of pounds. Much of the money was subscribed by charitable individuals. Much of it, too, came from the King Edward's Hospital Fund for London. And a certain amount

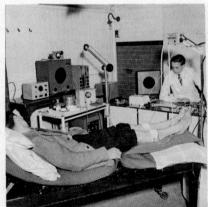

The new century saw a great development in methods of treatment and diagnosis. (a) A deep X-ray therapy unit; (b) an amplifier for minute electrical disturbances in the muscles

was provided by the patients themselves through the medium of the lady almoners.

Of the hospital's physicians and surgeons during the reigns of King Edward VII and King George V, the best-known were Sir Cuthbert Wallace, Sir Percy Sargent, Rowley Bristowe, Sir Maurice Cassidy, and Sir George Makins. But at least as important as the distinguished physicians and surgeons attached to St. Thomas's was Dame Alicia Lloyd Still, Matron of St. Thomas's and Superintendent of the Nightingale Training School from 1913-1937. She was made Sister Charity before she completed her three years' training at the special request of that famous physician Sir Seymour Sharkey, and was promoted to the post of ward sister in 1898 by Florence Nightingale herself. Utter devotion to the patients made her a somewhat exacting sister, for she demanded the highest possible standard of work from her juniors and saw that it was performed to the most finished detail. Soon after the private block was opened for paying patients she became sister in charge. (St. Thomas's was the first Hospital to have a home for private patients. In those days they paid three guineas a week and one guinea for the theatre, compared with the seven guineas paid in 1939.) Next she became Matron of Brompton Hospital and then Lady Superintendent of Middlesex Hospital, where she experimented with a number of administrative and nursing reforms which she rapidly put into execution when appointed Matron of St. Thomas's. Under the auspices of the Nightingale Fund Council the three-year curriculum was modernized and placed under the direction of its own executive officer, to whom Dame Alicia gave the title of Sister Tutor.

This comprehensive course, in which the sciences and arts relating to medicine and surgery as applied to Nursing were taught by university lecturers, came into being only a fortnight before the outbreak of World War I,

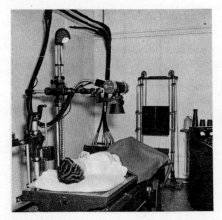

A modern installation for X-ray diagnosis (c), and (d) treatment of children in the massage school gymnasium. The photographs on these pages are taken in the post-war Hospital

57

but in spite of extra calls on the nursing staff, it was continued successfully. These demands came from a five-hundred-bed military hospital, largely hutted, which was attached to St. Thomas's, and staffed entirely by Nightingale nurses past and present. Ultimately, Dame Alicia Lloyd Still's curriculum became the basis of the examination syllabus in general nursing compiled by the General Nursing Council which had been set up in 1920 to administer the Nurses' Act, 1919. Previously, in 1916, Dame Alicia had helped to found the College of Nursing which later received the Royal Charter in recognition of its contribution to nursing education.

Florence Nightingale could not have wished for anyone better to follow up and expand her original pioneer work in nursing. Dame Alicia had the same creative instructive vision and forceful urge. Under her energetic guidance were opened many new departments directly related to social welfare in preventive medicine, extending the usefulness of St. Thomas's Hospital over a wide area of Public Health Services. Among her many distinctions were the award of the Florence Nightingale International Medal of the League of Red Cross Societies, and the Presidency of the International Council of Nurses. Her unswerving loyalty to the principles laid down by Florence Nightingale, and her interpretation of them in terms of modern thought and progress, together with her own selfless devotion in the cause of nursing at its highest, made her truly worthy to bear the mantle of the great foundress of modern nursing.

During her lifetime the average cost of an Out-Patient treatment rose steadily and since her death it has quadrupled; while the average cost of an in-patient to the Hospital has amounted to no less than ten guineas a week. These higher charges are due not only to the actual cost of medicines, bandages, and the like, but also—very properly—to the increased salaries of the nurses, sisters, and ward sisters. The latter formerly received £70 a year. Now, under the Rushcliffe Award, they receive £160 a year.

From the opening of the Hospital on its present site until the World War II, the first-year probationers lived in the Nightingale Home in the care of a Home Sister. During the year they were under very careful supervision as regards their health and general well-being; hours of duty were shorter than those of the more senior student nurses and one special feature was the hour given them for their tea, which they prepared for themselves, each nurse being provided with a teapot and tea for her special use. At the end of the year the probationers went on a month's holiday, from which they returned as staff nurses for the remainder of their training.

They were then housed in Gassiot House and in dormitories above the wards, and had a more independent existence. Their hours of duty were longer, and only half an hour was allowed for any meal. Life in the Nightingale Home ceased when the bombing of this Hospital began in 1940, and the destruction of the Home has prevented the segregation of probationers in one building, although it is hoped that a larger and more beautiful Nightingale Home may be built in the future.

X

THE CATASTROPHE OF WAR

At the time of the Munich crisis, every London hospital began to prepare for war. The planning was twofold—partly dispersal, so that the hospitals could move out into the country and accommodate wounded from overseas, as well as patients evacuated from London; and partly A.R.P. arrangements to deal with air-raid casualties in the London hospitals. It was obvious that St. Thomas's would be a sitting target for German bomber pilots, so a section of the basement, used as a linenry sorting room, was earmarked for an emergency operating theatre and by August 1939 this had been fitted up.

It was now apparent that war was imminent, and as the result of a very gloomy one o'clock news bulletin over the B.B.C., the staff decided to test this theatre to see how it would work in war-time conditions. So a week before Mr. Chamberlain told us that we were at war with Germany, two cases were operated on in the emergency theatre and it was discovered that the ventilation was inadequate. After this, proper ventilation was installed.

On 28th August, 1939, the Minister of Health directed that hospital admissions be restricted to acute cases only and that careful check be kept on the condition of patients who would have to be moved if evacuation were ordered. For though at least 25,000 casualties were expected daily from air raids on the metropolis, the public was not to know of these prudently conceived preparations until after war had broken out.

A few days after the morning of 3rd September, the Emergency Medical Services came into being. Under this scheme, prepared by the Ministry of Health, London and its outlying districts were divided into ten sectors with one or more of the larger London teaching hospitals at the head of each. St. Thomas's became the key hospital for Sector VIII, which included fifty-one voluntary hospitals and homes together with a miscellany of municipal institutions in South-west London and the adjoining parts of Surrey and Hampshire. Moreover, the Matron was appointed Sector Matron and was personally responsible for providing the nursing staff of all these hospitals.

St. Thomas's was also scheduled as a Casualty Clearing Station; 330 beds were to be maintained of which 200 were to be reserved and paid for by the Ministry of Health. Sixteen of the upper wards were closed and the allotted quota of beds was distributed over the remaining ten wards.

The Casualty Department was temporarily closed as its glass roof afforded inadequate protection against air attack, and the casualty service was incorporated in the Surgical Out-Patient Department. With the exception of the Tuberculosis and Venereal Disease sections, the Out-Patient services were suspended. The main operating theatres on the top floor were closed and an emergency four-table theatre opened in the basement where the linenry had once been. Windows were darkened and taped; dimmed lamps fitted to all entrances; 30,000 sandbags were filled and put in position; staff rotas were compiled for patrol work during raids.

Day and night staffs were organized for all departments. The Preliminary Training School for nurses evacuated to Shamley Green, near Guildford. A hundred student nurses went to Park Prewett Hospital near Basingstoke, together with a number of Nightingale sisters under whom their training could be continued. Second, third and fourth year nurses were evacuated to the Sector Hospitals at Woking, Chertsey, Pyrford and Epsom. St. Thomas's House and the paying patients' rooms were closed. The school of Physiotherapy dispersed and received hospitality at the Royal Infirmary, Manchester. Eighty-two members of the Ambulance Train service and the River Emergency Service were billeted in Riddell House.

As for the Medical School, under the Emergency Medical Scheme all civilian beds (except for acute cases) were closed, and almost all the special Out-Patients' services were suspended, so that it became impossible to provide for adequate clinical instruction. The School, with the support of the Ministry of Health, appealed to the associate Hospitals in the sector for help in providing continuity of training, and the Surrey County Council came forward immediately with practical suggestions. As a result, the clinical section was allowed facilities at the Kingston County Hospital, while other students found a welcome refuge in the Sector Hospitals, particularly Botleys Park War Hospital, and Pyrford Orthopædic Hospital with whom St. Thomas's had for many years been associated. The pre-clinical students were evacuated to Wadham College, Oxford, leaving only the pre-medical School in London, who were joined by King's College Hospital 1st M.B. Class.

But the expected blitz did not materialize and attendances at the hospital soon increased to the normal figures. Full Out-Patient services had to be restored and the Ministry of Health sanctioned the establishment of 200 civilian beds. This number justified the resumption of clinical teaching in London and by the middle of March 1940 the Medical School was again functioning in London.

Life continued thus for some months, and in spite of the dispersal of departments, patients continued to attend for treatment. Evacuees began trickling back, requiring the resumption of many of the services that had been suspended. The doors of St. Thomas's had always been open; it was impossible to think of them ever being shut. Out-Patient attendances began to increase. The clinics were in full swing. The school of Physiotherapy started up again. Everyone settled down to the familiar way of life.

During this period, many A.R.P. practices were carried out all over London. At St. Thomas's these practices were made very real by collecting all the hernias and less important operations so that twenty-six or thirty operations could be carried out in rapid succession, and the A.R.P. team-work perfected. Yet when the blitzkrieg came to London, nothing worked according to plan or practice in any hospital, and St. Thomas's was no exception.

Dame Alicia Lloyd Still, Matron of St. Thomas's and Superintendent of the Nightingale Training School from 1913 to 1937

Oil painting by George Harcourt

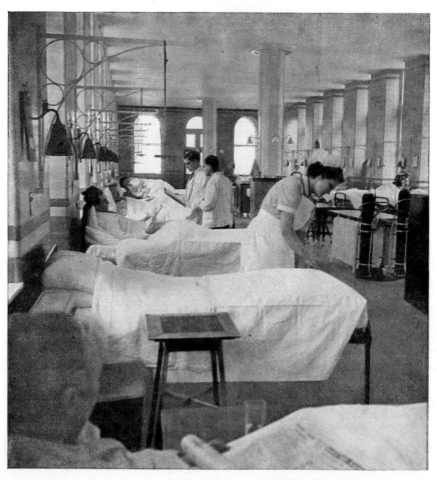

Morning in Nuffield Ward, restored after bombing

At 2.30 a.m. on Monday, September 9th, 1940, a large bomb dropped in the centre of the north side of the Hospital close to Westminster Bridge. Three floors collapsed and two nurses and four masseuses were crushed in the masonry. The Transformer Room, supplying the lifts and X-Ray Departments, was cut off. Seventy-six patients, well enough to be sent home, were discharged. The remainder were moved down to improvised wards in the basements of Blocks 2 and 4. Then the water supply failed. Nothing remained but for the immediate transfer of all patients to the Sector Hospitals. The water supply was restored in time to make it possible to retain fifty beds for casualties in the basements of Blocks 2 and 3.

From the experience gained in this first incident, the governors decided upon further precautions. Block 7 basement became a dormitory for Medical Students acting as stretcher bearers and dressers. The Massage School was evacuated. Block 4 Diet Classroom was fitted out as a Children's Ward with seven cots, and the main classroom became a dormitory for nurses.

No bombs fell on the next three nights, but Friday the 13th was particularly unlucky for the Hospital. At 3.15 a.m. two heavy bombs fell almost simultaneously. One struck the north side of "Jericho" where the maids were then living, the other (which did not go off until two hours later) falling in the Archbishop's Gardens. Both caused severe falls of masonry and widespread destruction of windows in Blocks 7 and 8. The accommodation problem was now critical; Riddell House assimilated twenty five of the maids, but the remaining thirty-five from "Jericho" had to sleep on mattresses on the floor in the Nurses' Dormitory in Block 4 basement.

But for an extraordinary coincidence, the present Matron might have been killed outright. She and an administrative sister took it in turns to go round the Hospital at night to see that all was well. Her shift started at three o'clock and she was about to start her round when she paused for a moment to adjust her cap. As she walked along the corridor the bomb dropped a few yards ahead of her and a kind of tidal wave of rubble and masonry spread out at exactly the point where she would have been had she not paused. She dashed to the quarters where the maids were sleeping and fortunately was able to account for all, as they were on the ground floor and basement. One however sustained serious injuries.

Two evenings later, on Sunday September 15th, at 8.30 p.m., the Theatre staff were preparing to operate on a policeman for acute appendicitis in the Emergency Operating Theatre when the Alert sounded. Almost simultaneously a bomb crashed down penetrating into the basement, killing one nurse and two house surgeons, and causing 52 casualties among the Hospital staff. Those in the Operating Theatre neither heard nor felt anything, they merely experienced that vague sensation that people have when they are coming round from an anæsthetic after a dental extraction. The lights had gone out, but someone found an emergency light and torches were produced. The Operating Theatre was a shambles, and so it was decided to operate in a small room in the Electrical Department further along in the basement.

Meantime, steam was spurting from the huge pipes in the basement ceiling—and gas leaking; in the Dispensary a fire was raging and appeared to be spreading; glass and rubble were strewn everywhere; and all the instrument cupboards were shattered. Everybody was so dirty that it was impossible to recognize anyone by the flickering torchlight. The Theatre sister was endeavouring to collect sufficient equipment to carry on with the operation as soon as possible and it was not until some time later that she discovered that one of her most able helpers, climbing over the debris and rescuing the various instruments, was none other than Sir Maurice Cassidy. She herself had been badly bruised, though she was unaware of this at the time and the only feeling she experienced was one of intense anger. The bomb, it was later discovered, had secured a direct hit on the centre of the building, penetrating to the basement, wrecking the Out-Patients' block, the College House sitting-room, the kitchen, the canteen and the administrative block and putting all the essential hospital services out of action.

The night nurses on this occasion had just finished their evening meal and had gone to another part of the building, otherwise they would have been killed. The present Secretary was making a personal tour of the Hospital at 4 a.m. to see that the staff were all right, when the Kitchen Superintendent stopped him in Riddell House. "I'm *so* glad to see you," she said with a sigh of relief. "I'd heard that they'd found your legs in the Dispensary." Thinking it over afterwards, the Secretary wondered moodily what could have made anyone think that they were *his* legs, rather than those of anyone else.

Official recognition was paid to three members of the staff for their gallantry. The George Medal was awarded to:—

H. R. B. Norman, M.B., B.CH., M.R.C.S., L.R.C.P., Resident Assistant Physician.

P. B. Maling, Medical Student.

H. E. Frewer, Assistant Clerk of Works, St. Thomas's Hospital, London.

The citation read:—

After St. Thomas's Hospital had been hit by an H.E. bomb it was found that two of the Staff were trapped. Mr. Frewer formed a rescue party and was joined by Dr. Norman and Mr. Maling.

The debris had crashed through the ground floor into the basement. The Dispensary stores had been destroyed and the alcohol and acids caught fire. Gas was escaping and masonry was continually falling. Mr. Frewer led the rescue party. Dr. Norman, assisted by Mr. Maling, burrowed into the debris and gave morphia injections. They succeeded in extricating the casualties.

The emergency operating theatre in the basement was refitted and was the only operating theatre in use through the whole of the war. (It was still being used for two years after VJ-Day, all the other operating theatres having been put out of action by bombs.)

Once again it was necessary to effect the total evacuation of hospital patients. Next morning the Clerk of Works and the Engineer's staff started

At 2.30 a.m. on Monday, September 9th, 1940, a large bomb dropped in the centre of the north side of the Hospital close to Westminster Bridge. Three floors collapsed

clearing up the basements. By evening they were not only cleared, but water and electricity had been restored. Their success was shortlived. During the night that followed, a violent explosion blew in all the plaster-board windows of Block 2 basement ward and it was again necessary to inform the Group Officer that St. Thomas's was unable to provide fifty casualty beds.

For a month the hospital was spared any further destruction and the work of extempore repairs was pushed forward. But troubles soon started again, and on 15th October, soon after 9 o'clock in the morning, a heavy bomb struck the Northcote Trust Room, destroying a number of rooms on the staircase of Block VII, and again wrecking City Ward. The automatic telephone exchange was completely buried. The night was marked by heavy and incessant bombing in the vicinity of the hospital and the inflow of casualties became so unmanageable that the old bed-store in the basement had to be improvised to receive them and was called Scutari, because of its resemblance to the Crimean War Hospital.

But, apart from two severe incendiary raids, there were no further incidents that year. Nevertheless, the situation which faced the governors at the beginning of 1941 could hardly have been more discouraging. The Medical School was evacuated to the Guildford area; the majority of the student nurses were dispersed as also was the School of Physiotherapy, and

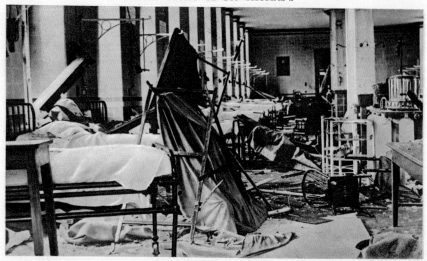

It seemed as though St. Thomas's had been singled out for destruction. High explosive, incendiary and flying bomb all took their toll. The wreckage in Albert Ward

the greater part of the special services had been entirely suspended. There was no prospect of returning to the old order, and it did not look at all unlikely that another bomb would put the hospital wholly out of commission. In this unpromising situation, the governors decided there could only be one answer: they must find alternative accommodation outside London. Approaches were made to the Ministry of Health and the London County Council.

The Emergency Hospital at Hydestile, Godalming, adjoining the King George V Sanatorium, had recently been occupied by the Australians. To adapt it to their own purpose required extensive structural alterations. Nevertheless, when the Minister of Health offered the lease to the governors, they gratefully accepted it. Four new huts were built. Properties were bought and leased in the neighbourhood to house the staff. A shuttle service was arranged between the two hospitals. Equipment was transferred, and on 17th April, 1941, the first convoy of patients left London for Hydestile.

Even this operation was not carried out without interruption. On 16th April, soon after sunset, London had again been raided. Showers of incendiaries set fire to many of the Hospital buildings, causing among other incidents the total destruction of the carpenter's shop. Heavy bombs fell in the river, shaking the building and smashing nearly every window on the river side. At 2.30 a.m., a land-mine exploded in Nightingale Square between Blocks 2 and 3, bringing down the Sanitary Tower of Block 2 and the colonnade joining Blocks 2 and 3, as well as destroying the Nightingale Home. The interiors of these two blocks were entirely wrecked together with the basement wards of Nuffield and Arthur. Nuffield was flooded and the Ophthalmic ward above Arthur caught fire. Gas, electricity and water all failed, and the emergency lighting installation had to be brought into operation. Notwithstanding the appalling destruction of the night, no patients were hurt and on the following morning the first batch of twenty to leave for the country passed through the hospital gates.

The ordeal was still not over. On 10th May the Alert sounded. It was to bring the worst raid of the whole war. At intervals of only a few minutes at a time, until 5 o'clock the following morning, sticks of high explosives and countless hundreds of incendiaries poured down on the hospital and its immediate surroundings. The main buildings received three direct hits from medium-calibre bombs. Riddell House was hit twice. A bomb fell in the garage yard. The whole of the top floor of Block 4 was burned out. Fire damaged the roof and first floor of St. Thomas's House. The garage, cars and timber store were burned to the ground. Casualties streamed in and space had to be made for them in Arthur Ward which was only partially ready, Scutari having to be evacuated hurriedly through the flooding of the basement.

May 10th was calamitous. It was also, by a fortunate providence, the last raid for over three years in which St. Thomas's suffered any serious damage. Out of the question, as it was, to embark on any serious work of reconstruction, it gave the hospital breathing-space in which to count its losses and plan for the future. The damage to buildings, disruption of services and dispersal of patients have been spoken of, but very little has been said of the work which never ended.

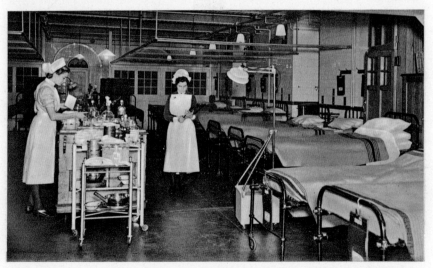

The emergency ward for women casualties in the basement of the massage department.
Tidying is completed after the transfer of casualties to a sector hospital

The doors of St. Thomas's were never closed. And even in the worst days of confusion, the normal work of treating out-patients went on, quietly and smoothly, with little regard for the fortunes of war. Apparently there was nothing that could discourage the regular out-patient from attending his regular clinic or receiving his regular treatment—nothing that could persuade him that St. Thomas's was not still, as it has always been, the place where he would be welcomed and given the attention he needed. War casualties, naturally, were accepted at all times. But the regularity with which normal daily attendances were maintained, often with the dust and rubble of the night's bombing still uncleared, with water and light failing, and the few remaining beds herded into basements, displayed a touching faith in the inviolability of St. Thomas's which few who saw it will forget.

The lull came to an end on 4th July, 1944, when a flying bomb fell behind Riddell House and St. Thomas's House. On the 15th July another bomb hit the theatre in Adelaide Ward in Block 2 causing further extensive damage to Mary Ward, Matron's House, and the Nightingale Home. Block 2 staircase and the corridor were completely destroyed. The blast caused damage as far away as Block 8. Most of the Administrative offices were made unusable. Nuffield Ward in the basement of Block 2 was evacuated and the patients hastily transferred to an improvised ward in the Massage School gymnasium.

The war ended; but the toll it had taken was immeasurable. To many, indeed, it seemed almost as though St. Thomas's had been singled out for destruction. Nor was this surprising. The endless twists and bends of the River Thames almost certainly caused the Luftwaffe pilots to mistake St. Thomas's Hospital for the hated House of Commons immediately across the river. It is probable that each of the bombs dropped by piloted aircraft on the hospital was intended for the Palace of Westminster.

Yet the hospital has survived its ordeal. And in recalling those days, one must also recall the fine courage and tenacity of the hospital's war-time staff. Under conditions of most appalling danger and discomfort they carried out their duties with gallantry and determination. *Thanks largely to their loyalty not a single patient was lost through enemy action.* But among their own numbers there were those who gave their lives.*

If you ask the sisters who remained on duty at St. Thomas's all through the war about their war experiences, they mention a great many dates and statistical figures in rather an aloof manner, but the moment they start to talk about their porters and their "pink ladies", their faces light up and their voices become enthusiastic. The "pink ladies" are the daily domestic workers who wear pink striped uniforms, and even after the worst raids the "pinkies" always turned up the following morning to sweep up the hospital. Even if their own homes had been damaged—which they often were—the hospital came first and they never failed to appear at the time they were expected.

---

* Nurse K. M. Forbes, Nurse S. E. Durham, Nurse C. G. Walker, Miss M. Doucet, Miss B. Mortimer Thomas, Miss S. Dunn, Miss G. Lockyer, Dr. J. C. K. Campbell, Dr. P. B. Spilsbury.

The debris of war remains. St. Thomas's is not yet repaired but much has been done to put the Hospital into commission again. There were casualties among the staff, but not a single patient was lost through enemy action

XI

THE THRESHOLD OF CHANGE

Nobody who has passed over Westminster bridge can have failed to be horrified by the mangled buildings of St. Thomas's Hospital, but few passers-by can have any idea of what splendid plans are being prepared by the governors and their architects for the future of the hospital. Generally speaking, it is proposed to increase the number of floors of the four central blocks, link them together with a communicating wing in which all the administrative offices will be placed and add, near the surgical wards, a new block of operating theatres grouped in pairs on each floor. The main corridor of the hospital will be about two hundred yards long, less than two-thirds of its original length, and this saving of the time and energy of the staff will be further increased by the provision of more and better lifts. In addition, the present basement level of the hospital will be cleared as far as possible of obstructing buildings and embankments, so as to admit light and sun and a glimpse of greenery to the members of the staff who work there.

When the new central block has been carried to a certain stage, it will be possible to begin the rebuilding of the Medical School on the site of the Treasurer's House, the damaged shell of which stands at the head of Westminster Bridge opposite the south side of County Hall. More room will be found here than is available on the existing congested site at the other end of the hospital opposite Lambeth Palace. The new building will be of a height and bulk suitable to balance the south-west angle of County Hall. As it is very likely that with the eventual replacement of trams by buses, the short length of Stangate will be closed, and York Road carried directly across Westminster Bridge Road into the Lambeth Palace Road, the frontage of the new school can later be extended almost as far as the York Road junction. The building can then offer complete facilities for students and research workers, including laboratories which are at present housed in the hospital itself.

The most important developments outside the main block of the hospital proper, will be those for the recreation and residence of staff and students, in which additional and improved accommodation for sisters and nurses must have absolute priority. In a large teaching hospital such as St. Thomas's, with traditions earned and maintained over centuries, the corporate life of the working community is second in importance only to the welfare of the patients to which in fact it is dedicated. It is intended that the buildings shall give expression to this corporate unity in their layout; and though the residential group must remain an integral part of the hospital, it will have an individuality of its own and will take advantage of all the amenities that a central urban situation will allow.

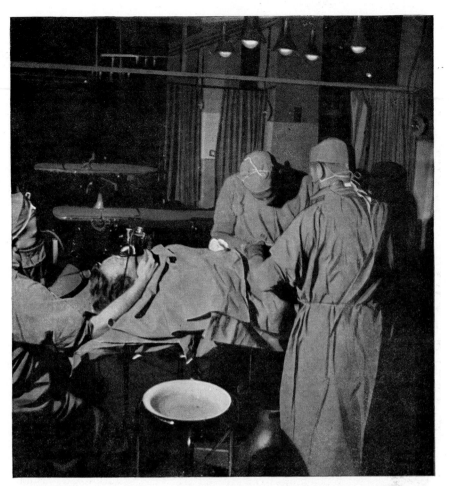

An operation in progress in one of the war-time basement theatres still in use.
The surgeon and his assistants wear green overalls to lessen the glare

St. Thomas's Hospital today. A photograph taken from the roof of Scotland Yard

Broadly, it is proposed to group the accommodation for sisters and nurses, including the Preliminary Training School and Educational Department on and around Paris Street and the existing Riddell House, taking advantage of southern aspect and wherever possible of trees and gardens, and setting aside a relatively quiet situation for night nurses. Medical student accommodation, on the other hand, including three small residential colleges and common rooms and refectories, will be grouped on and around Stangate Street, opposite the School. Accommodation to be shared by staff and students, such as the assembly hall, the swimming bath and various other recreational amenities, will be situated between these two groups, disposed around a "green", the hall having access from the road and thus taking advantage of public transport.

From the patients' point of view, as well as for efficiency of nursing, the most interesting single item is likely to be the typical ward plan. It is proposed to maintain the present structure, with its great room height giving light and sun and cross-ventilation, but to sub-divide the main ward into smaller wards by a flexible arrangement which will enable single beds to be isolated, or convalescent cases to be grouped in sub-wards of four or six. A corridor, external to the ward itself, will provide alternative circulation and will give access to all the sanitary accommodation on the north side, leaving all the south-facing windows clear. In addition, two new features are to be added to each ward. One is a treatment and dressing room situated near the middle of each ward; the other is an extended sun-room, facing south and west, and giving a view from all wards of the river and the Houses of Parliament.

Out-patients (who are more numerous at St. Thomas's than at any other London hospital) will have a new entrance hall from Lambeth Palace Road and will also have a view of the river as soon as they come into the waiting room. They will, in fact, have a large proportion of the present ground floor reserved for them. The Governors' Hall and the Chapel will retain their central position, but will be kept back so as to interfere as little as possible with the lighting of the main ward blocks and will be moved on to a higher floor than they occupy at present.

An investigation is to be made of the possibilities of heating the entire hospital and its ancillary buildings by means of a system of heat pumps, using the water of the Thames. Complete air-conditioning is to be provided for the Out-Patients' Department, the theatres, and certain other parts of the hospital; using the most modern method of removing dust from the air before it passes into the treated rooms. The wards will be heated by low-temperature radiant panels, topped up by occasional gas or electric fires at points where these are also demanded for the sake of sociability.

The theatres are two to a floor, sharing a common sterilizing room with separate clean and dirty circulation. They are designed to provide clear and unconfused lines of movement and to give ready access to services.

This whole programme has to be devised in such a way that it can be carried out by stages, without interfering with the essential work of the hospital.

At least one block of the present wards will remain for some time as a "decanting station", to take care of patients and staff removed from the wards successively under reconstruction. This plan for reconstruction will provide a teaching hospital of 1,000 beds, besides additional beds for paying patients. On this basis, the hospital will be re-established to continue and extend its historic work for the care of the sick and the development of medicine.

It is difficult to prophesy how the nursing of a big teaching hospital will be affected when taken over by the Government. But it is hoped that, however controlled it may be, it will be allowed to keep the spirit of the tradition of service. To enable this the Matron must still have power of selection of candidates for nursing training. Having herself gone through every stage of this training, who could be better fitted to make a right selection? The Government wants the best for the patient, therefore the standard of nursing must remain high. This has suffered to a certain degree during the years of the War when student nurses were scattered throughout the Sector and their training lacked continuity, but this we hope is of the past. A wise Government will see to it that the Nightingale Training School, the first of its kind in the country, where over 1,100 applications are received annually for roughly 100 vacancies, shall continue to train nurses to serve mankind in the best possible manner and continue to be a vital part of the Health Service of the country.

It is, of course, too early to judge what effect the proposed State Medical Service will have on the future intake of medical students. Will medicine still

The student nurses are now back in the parent Hospital. It is hoped that under the new order the Nightingale Training School may continue its work of service

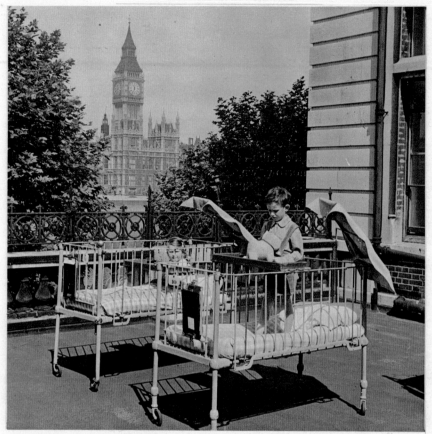

In 1948, Westminster is to become more than a symbol in the life of the Hospital. But the spirit of its staff and the deep trust of its patients will remain

attract the type of young man that it has attracted in the past? If it does, and if the Dean is to be allowed the same powers of selection of medical students as hitherto, there is nothing to fear in this direction from the nationalization of the Hospital. The Medical School of St. Thomas's will keep its individuality and form an integral part of the University of London.

In addition to its local and parochial work for the sick poor, St. Thomas's has always had a much wider influence; its doctors and nurses have gone to all parts of the country and to all countries of the world. Patients, too, have come to St. Thomas's from all parts of Great Britain. There may in the new service be some restriction in the region from which patients may come, but there will be no limitation to the spread of the St. Thomas's spirit in the women and men trained in its schools.

What of the patient? For centuries he has put his trust in the voluntary hospitals, because in every true Englishman's make-up there is a deep love of tradition and for nearly eight hundred years the Londoner could be sure that St. Thomas's was a place where he would be welcomed and given the treatment he needed.

He proved this during the blitzkrieg when he refused to be put off from attending his ordinary clinic on the usual day, merely because his particular department had been bombed into rubble. It has mattered little to him whether the physicians and surgeons have worn priests' robes or white coats. Through the centuries, Londoners have known the nursing sisters of St. Thomas's, whether in the habit of a nun or in the blue-and-white spotted dress of to-day. Tomorrow, whatever the uniform worn, they will still remain, above all, the Sisters of St. Thomas's Hospital. They will continue to refer to Florence Nightingale as Miss Nightingale and, to them, nursing will remain a vocation, as distinct from a profession. This, perhaps, is the surest guarantee of all that, so long as London stands, St. Thomas's will equal and may even outshine the glorious achievements of the past.